C000128209

THE BOOK OF

HYPNOSIS

DAVID LESSER

By the same author:

HYPNOTHERAPY EXPLAINED (1985)
ISBN 0 9510875 1 7

The Book of HYPNOSIS
© Copyright David Lesser
First Published 1989
Reprinted 1999
ISBN 0 9510875 2 5

Published by
Curative Hypnotherapy Examination Committee
8 Balaclava Road, Kings Heath, Birmingham B14 7SG

Printed by
Mercian Manuals
353 Kenilworth Road, Balsall Common
Coventry CV7 7DL

Contents

Chapter   Page

Contents

Foreword

Many people who had read my first book subsequently asked me when I would be producing another one.

I replied that I was a Hypnotherapist not a writer, and that I had written everything that I wanted to impart. I genuinely felt I could add nothing further to the literature on Hypnosis.

Gradually, however, the need to write this present volume has grown within me. I know that I shall never be a writer in the accepted sense of the word but I also know that I am a good Hypnotherapist and, judging by the number of people who come to me for treatment after experiencing poor and unthinking use of hypnosis, further enlightenment is a necessity for the public.

Hypnotherapists are human. They are subject to normal failings and weaknesses. It is for this reason that I have included my sketches in this volume – to show that even in a serious book we can have a sense of humour – or is vanity the failing that makes me human?

I hope my readers will find a greater understanding within these pages.

With this publication, I now firmly believe that I have said everything that I have to contribute on the subject of using Hypnosis to actually cure as well as covering other aspects of the subject. But I make no promises . . .

The Hypnotic Feeling

Fools have played with it, knowledgeable people have experimented with it, charlatans have made money out of it and comedians have boosted their egos with it. Yet none of them can satisfactorily explain it.

Journalists have made blaring headlines out of it, the medical profession appears to feel threatened by it, those interested in the occult have tricked people with it and well-meaning therapists have alleviated symptoms with it. Yet the number of people who use it to maximum advantage is very small indeed.

People with little apparent experience have written books about it and some have even set up training courses and persuaded gullible members of the public to part with their hard-earned cash (often in considerable amounts) to learn very little about it.

The most effective weapon in the armoury of any therapist is Hypnosis, yet it is also the most widely misunderstood of any treatment.

It can be used to cure totally and permanently a wide variety of problems yet even those who are using it every day in attempts to help others, very rarely appear to understand the real power for good they have in their possession.

The reasons for this are many and one of them was summed up in a letter I received from a Hypnotherapist who had a practice in the same part of the country as my own. She wrote to say that she was moving out of the region and wanted to hand over her list of regular patients to another Hypnotherapist.

As soon as I saw the words "regular patients" I consigned her letter to the waste-paper bin as a Hypnotherapist should not have people coming for treatment over a long period and I assumed that what she really wanted to do was to sell a regular income. However, a few minutes later I rescued her communication and telephoned her as I thought it might be worth-while finding out to what use she was putting Hypnosis.

Although she looked very professional, it appeared that this lady was not really committed to Hypnotherapy as, in spite of having been in practice for a few years and in spite of her "regular patients" she only had sufficient people coming for treatment to hire a room for a couple of half-day sessions each week. But the really distressing part of our interview was the pride she expressed in the number of people who had been coming to her for treatment for over a year and a half. Obviously, she must have been doing them some good even if it was only to devote time to listening to them but, just as obviously, the help she was giving her 'patients' was very limited and she either lacked a proper understanding of the use of hypnosis to best effect, or her interest was really in financial gain.

To learn how to hypnotise a person takes only a few minutes, but hypnosis is only a tool and it can be used in many ways. The internal combustion engine can be used in an ambulance to rush someone to hospital to save their life or it can be used for death and destruction when driving a tank on the battle-field. It could also be put to an innocuous half-way use just for pleasure, to take a family on a picnic. In a similar way hypnosis can be used simply to induce a temporarily beneficial state of relaxation, or to suppress symptoms, or for therapeutic visualisation – but it can also be used to CURE, although it is this latter use that so many people find hard to accept.

One can understand the medical profession, with their years of very hard training, looking with a slightly jaundiced eye when you point out that simple logic will often permanently get rid of the illness for which they have been prescribing medicine for 9 or 10 years, yet an increasing number are recommending people for treatment as they see more and more worth-while results in their patients.

However, it is not just the medical profession who sometimes look askance at Curative Hypnotherapists. There are a very large number of people who are actually earning a living from the use of hypnosis who will not use their minds to THINK and are just prepared to go on using this tool in the way they have been taught. It does appear that more hypnotherapists are beginning to realise that they have the ability to help a sufferer lose their problem for ever, and one of the most encouraging signs of this is that on my recent training courses, a quarter of the trainees have been people who had gone through other courses where they had been taught to suppress symptoms or get the patient to fit some theory or other. However, these people had the intelligence to think and realised that there had to be more benefits to hypnosis than their previous teachers had told them. Hence their attendance in Birmingham.

In my previous book "Hypnotherapy Explained" (Curative Hypnotherapy Examination Committee) I attempted to describe the state of hypnosis but, for those who have not read it, a brief description seems to be called for here.

The first thing to do when trying to explain what hypnosis feels like is to forget the jargon about 'altered states of consciousness' and 'trance'. These are meaningless words when all you are talking about is a beautiful state of relaxation. It is nothing but that – an extremely beautiful state of relaxation in which you are aware and awake – aware of everything that is said and therefore have the ability to go along with the therapists' words or reject them.

That decision is yours and, because you are aware of everything, it is always yours no matter how deeply relaxed you become.

To achieve this state of relaxation it is necessary for you to accept what the Hypnotherapist says, to go along with his words. It is only commonsense that no-one can **force** you into relaxation – your automatic reaction to being forced is to fight back, which is in no way relaxing. A therapist cannot force you to become relaxed, he can only **guide** you into relaxation. You have the choice as to whether you follow his guidance or not.

Having been prepared to accept and become relaxed, how do you feel? You feel just that – relaxed. You are in that half-way stage between being asleep and being awake. A drowsy, day-dreamy state. An absolutely natural state in which you know everything that is going on and hear and understand everything that is being said but will only bother about it if it is really important to you.

It is a state that you have to go through every time you go to sleep and again every time you wake up. So anyone old enough to read this has experienced this state thousands of times and the only difference on this occasion is that you will achieve it by following the suggestions of someone else, and that by continuing to follow his suggestions you will stay in this state long enough to really enjoy it whereas, when you are going to sleep in the normal way (or waking up normally), you usually pass through this relaxation too quickly to really appreciate it.

So forget about being taken over, or being controlled (if I could do this I would have an appointment with my bank manager first thing tomorrow morning and be retired in the lap of luxury by the weekend). Forget about being turned into a Zombie or feeling the therapist's mind groping around inside your own. You are just accepting, with the ability to reject at any moment you choose.

Knowing that you can and will reject anything that does not suit you the therapist will, naturally, only ask you to go along with things that he knows are acceptable to you. You have the control but he doesn't want you to use it. The important thing is that **you** have control and knowing that means that you do not have to exercise it.

A large number of people, after experiencing hypnosis for the first time insist that they were not hypnotised because, as they say, "I heard every word". They believe that they should become unconscious, or that they should be 'taken over'.

No matter how much one may discuss what is going to happen before helping a person to achieve this beautiful state of relaxation, many still have pre-conceived ideas and believe that something dramatic should happen. They have difficulty in accepting that we are only aiming to achieve a state of relaxation. A state on the way towards, but this side of, sleep. It is so un-dramatic that, when you go to bed at night, you do not even realise that you drifted through this state into sleep until you wake up the following morning!

If you are about to experience hypnosis for the first time, the most important thing you can do is to accept. That is the key word - ACCEPT.

Do not try to relax. That involves effort and therefore is not relaxing.

Do not worry about how relaxed you are. Worry, too, is counter-productive. Leave your relaxation up to your therapist. A good therapist will know; he or she will be looking for physical signs of relaxation. I have no difficulty in recognising when a patient is sufficiently relaxed but I certainly cannot recognise when I have reached that state myself. If I, who spend my life helping people achieve this relaxation before we commence treatment, cannot discern when I am 'in hypnosis', what chance does the uninitiated have?

Leave it up to your therapist to watch for the signs of relaxation. Do not analyse — analysis requires concentration and concentration is an enemy of relaxation. Just accept and you will very quickly drift into a truly gorgeous state of relaxation.

One cannot give a precise description of this state of relaxation. Our normal feeling of tension or readiness, whether for work or going to a party, is somewhat different to that of other people and we measure our feelings of relaxation against this normal state. Therefore the experience of hypnosis will be slightly different to everyone. But, I repeat, it is a state of relaxation in which you are awake and aware of what is going on and in which you have the ability to accept or reject.

The relaxation of hypnosis is not only pleasant but is beneficial to everyone. However, hypnosis is only a tool — and a tool that can be used in several different ways as we shall see.

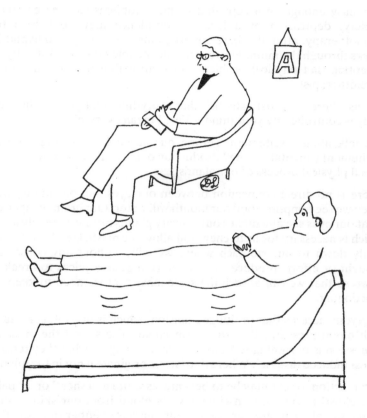

"I wasn't hypnotised – I heard every word you said"

Mind Power

Everyone benefits from relaxation, but the relaxation of hypnosis can, **in the right hands,** be a very powerful tool in helping people get rid of a wide variety of both mental and physical problems.

It is easy enough to accept that mental problems such as phobias, anxiety, depression or a lack of confidence may be helped by hypnotherapy; after all, these are problems of the mind and hypnosis works through the mind. However, some people may find difficulty in accepting that physical problems also fall within the province of a hypnotherapist.

Let us, therefore, first establish that everything that goes on in your body is controlled by your mind – Yes! I mean everything.

We talk about excitement 'getting our adrenaline flowing'. Is not excitement a mental feeling? Production of adrenaline is, however, an actual physical process of our glands.

There is no direct connection between our eyes and our mouth but when we see tempting food our mouth will water. Our brain recognises what our eyes see and makes our salivary glands produce the lubricant which is necessary for us to chew and allow the masticated food to slip easily down to our stomach where we will, without any conscious thought or effort, produce the necessary digestive juices to break it down so that we can absorb the sustenance that we need to keep us functioning.

Everyone accepts that prolonged tension, which is mental, can cause high blood pressure; that stress can create ulcers; and the medical profession is beginning to think that cancer may be what they term a 'stress induced disease'. Where does stress originate if not in the mind?

Our reaction to fear may be to become 'as white as a sheet' or 'as pale as a ghost' as our subconscious diverts blood from our skin to our muscles to allow us greater fuel for our muscles to either run from the danger or counteract it. Our breathing rate and heart rate will alter to provide more oxygen for our blood stream to take to our muscles to burn for the same purpose.

Maybe our 'bowels turn to water' (I feel this is more polite than the more modern expression) to lighten our body. We may become 'sick with fright' for the same purpose. Possibly our 'hair stands on end' to cool our body because of the excessive heat that may be produced by muscle activity during our flight or fight, and the sweating that will probably take place serves the same purpose.

Certainly our sexual feelings cease. Sexual arousal would not only divert attention away from whatever may be threatening us but requires quite a considerable diversion of blood to the sexual organs in both male and female. Our digestive processes also cease as they require considerable calories that we may need to survive.

Within the above few lines we have talked about blood pressure, cancer, adrenaline, ulcers, digestion and sweating. We have mentioned the effect in the mouth and on the skin, lungs, heart, bowels, stomach, sex organs and hair. All these effects are outside our conscious control yet are created by mental stimuli. They are all physical reactions caused by our mind, the automatic part of our mind – our subconscious – which is there to protect us.

Our subconscious also controls every muscle in our body. There is not a single muscle that we can operate directly by our conscious mind. When you lift your finger to scratch your nose, do you know how many muscles you use? Even forgetting for the moment the muscles you use to lift your upper arm, those that flex your forearm and those that get your wrist into the right position, you still have 14 joints in your fingers to position correctly. You probably curl three of your fingers towards the palm of your hand, bring your thumb across to rest on your middle finger while sticking your index finger out straight to accomplish the simple task of relieving a slight irritation.

You may have consciously wanted to scratch but the whole procedure requires so many muscle movements, and each movement requires a different amount of tension in the individual muscle that you need a computer to work it all out in anything like a reasonable amount of time.

And that is what you used: your computer – your subconscious mind. You consciously wanted to scratch, your computer-operator decided it needed to scratch, and it gave the necessary instruction to your computer.

I could fill page after page with examples, but I hope that the above may be sufficient for you to accept that everything in your body is controlled by your mind – and the part of your mind that does this controlling is your **subconscious.**

If the subconscious has this control, does it not appear logical to seek there for the cause of a malfunction unless it is created by an external cause such as a broken bone or a virus infection? **Everything that has no external cause must have an internal cause.**

Physical discomfort caused by tension is created by muscle contraction. Muscles contract when they get a message down their nerves. From where does this message originate if not in the mind? And does any individual want to experience the discomfort that a bad case of tension can cause? Do they consciously create these aches and pains? If not, then from what part of the mind do these message come?

I liken this part of the mind to a computer because, in essence, it reacts in the same way. When asked a question it can only give an answer in accordance with the information in its memory. It does not have the critical or analytical ability to do anything else. It works completely logically but without commonsense.

If a computer 'believes' that $2 + 2 = 5$ it will always give this as an answer, but things can get more complicated than that. Let us assume that a computer has this particular bit of wrong information and is asked to do the following sum:

$$\begin{array}{r} 2+ \\ 2+ \\ \underline{13} \\ \\ = \underline{} \end{array}$$

obviously the answer should be 17 but the computer 'believes' the first two numbers add up to 5 and, by adding 13, makes the answer 18.

However, let us assume that the identical information reaches the computer – but in a different order, thus:

$$\begin{array}{r} 2+ \\ 13+ \\ \underline{2} \\ \\ = \underline{} \end{array}$$

working on the numbers in sequence, the computer will add 2 and 13 and, as its misinformation only refers to $2 + 2$, will make the answer 15. It will then add on the last figure 2 and, again without any mis-information regarding the adding of 15 and two, will arrive at the correct answer of 17.

The computer itself cannot isolate the wrong information because it can only work on the information it has – and that information it 'believes'. It needs the commonsense of the computer-operator to correct the wrong answer and before the operator can do this he or she must be able to see what wrong information was entered in the first place.

Your sub-conscious reacts in this way – it has to react in accordance with the information that it has previously accepted.

If you can bear with my mathematics just a few moments longer I would like to take this a step further and see how errors can escalate out of all proportion using the same logic without the opportunity of bringing commonsense to bear:

With the same mis-information, our computer will 'believe' that:

$$2 \times 50 + 2 \text{ will equal } 102$$
(which is, of course, correct)

but, without commonsense, it will also believe that:

$$2 + 2 \times 50 \text{ will equal } 250$$

i.e. $2 + 2 = 5 \times 50 = 250$ – an error **50 times greater** than the original mis-information (original wrong data was $2 + 2 = 5$ – hence an error of only 1).

Now we are developing real problems, and if the wrong data is in the human mind, you may be beginning to realise how trouble starts to develop and how people can have different reactions to what appears to be the same situation.

We have to isolate the wrong original data before we can correct it and to achieve this we need the information from the computer not the computer-operator. The mis-information is in the computer itself so we do not want to know what interpretation the operator may have put on it. We need the actual wrong data.

This is the purpose of using hypnosis in therapy. To relax the computer-operator – the conscious mind – so that the therapist has direct access to the information in the computer; but all the time the conscious mind is aware of the questions being asked and of the answers given by the sub-conscious and is able to interrupt if this is really necessary.

If you go for hypnotherapy treatment, this relaxation is of your conscious mind, the part of your mind that is normally between the outside world (or therapist) and the part of your mind that reacts – your subsconscious. Your conscious mind analyses virtually everything you see or hear or physically feel, then refers to the memories stored in your sub-conscious to make a decision as to what action you should take. The object of using hypnosis in therapy is to relax this critical, analytical part of your mind so that you do not let it intrude into the treatment.

Consciously you should sit on the sidelines, aware of what is going on and able to intervene if you wish but allowing the Hypnotherapist direct access to the information in that part of your mind that reacts. After all that is the part that is causing your problem, isn't it? You haven't consciously made a decision to suffer your complaint have you? Yet panic, anxiety, phobias, depression, lack of confidence, or unnatural embarrassment (to take some of the obvious examples) are mental reactions and therefore have to be due to something in your mind.

So your conscious mind is a nuisance in therapy – let's give it a holiday while we find out from the part of your mind that controls your reactions just what is causing your problem. Remembering all the time that although your conscious mind is relaxed you still have the ability to step in between the therapist and your sub-conscious to stop either suggestions going in or information coming out.

In other words you will always have control. The same control as has the car driver following the directions of an outsider who is standing behind the car giving guidance as the vehicle is reversed into a small parking space.

The driver has temporarily relinquished control to the pedestrian but has the ability to disregard the instructions given and in hypnosis you will temporarily relinquish control to the therapist with the ability to take charge if you feel it advisable.

Under the guidance of the therapist you will achieve a good state of relaxation and the therapist should, no later than your second treatment, commence the task of finding out 'why'. If he doesn't, or starts trying to make you fit his theories then you should question just where this form of treatment will eventually lead.

Do not allow your therapist to put forward theories. The information in your mind is unique and **no-one will have experienced the identical events that you have.** Everything that happens you will interpret in the light of these past experiences, thus your interpretations are unique to you. Your problem is an incorrect reaction and just as you have created your problem, so you are the only one who can cure it. You do need help to do this but the necessary information is in your own mind – not in that of the therapist.

Although things may not be clear to you while undergoing treatment the full understanding should be yours by the completion. You will know how you created your trouble. You will understand WHY, – **and in that understanding lies your cure.**

Traumatic Events

"It's too late to fix it," said the Red Queen
"When you've once said a thing that fixes
it and you must take the consequences"
Lewis Carroll (Through the Looking Glass)

Now that we have established what it feels like to be hypnotised, let us take the bull by the horns and say at the beginning of this chapter that the really traumatic events in a persons life rarely cause problems.

As it is such a commonly held belief that events that cause problems must create uncomfortable emotions when they are recalled, maybe a few case histories will make my point – and two of these people were volunteers on just one training course so the cases described were fully witnessed by over a dozen other people apart from myself and the patients themselves. (I do not believe in teaching by lectures – the only way is to demonstrate the treatment by advertising for volunteers. If strangers with migraine, pre-menstrual tension, phobias and so on are cured in front of you, and you have seen and understood how and why they have created their problem and noted the techniques used then there can be no doubts in your mind. Everything is proven step by step).

MARY was about 8 years old when she saw her father beating her sister who was two years younger. When she remembered this event she cried in spite of my attempts to prevent this emotion getting in the way of treatment and slowing down our progress. This was the worst event Mary had ever experienced but the reason she reacted to that traumatic event in the way she did was because of her mothers' previous words to the effect that she wished Mary "had never been born". Those words started the belief that she was not wanted and it was a logical step from there to the belief that her mother may try to get rid of her.

When she saw her father trying to 'get rid of' her sister, she believed she would be the next on the list to be disposed of.

She had never liked her mother so her mothers' words that she did not want her were not unexpected and created no upset at the time they were spoken, but she loved her sister so there was trauma when she thought her father was getting rid of her, particularly when she imagined what was to follow when her father had finished the job in hand.

Mary recalled the father/sister event two sessions before bringing back her mother's words. She went back to that event because it was the bigger of the the two in her mind yet the words of her mother were the real cause of her problem. The incident where her father hurt her sister was the 'trigger' that caused her problem but, as I tried to make clear in "Hypnotherapy Explained", a good therapist will not take too much notice of triggers but go back to find out the event that loaded that persons 'gun' in the first place. To deal with a trigger is to leave the gun loaded for another trigger to activate it once more, whereas, if you go back and actually unload the gun, then no amount of trigger-pulling can make it fire.

Although Mary experienced emotion when recalling her father hurting her sister, she showed no emotion in recalling the real event that caused her problem. Her mother's words were not unexpected, therefore they did not hurt her.

GEORGE suffered from terrible headaches and anxiety. His anxiety caused him to be at work every day two hours before everyone else so that he was fully prepared long before they arrived. At the consultation he told me that he could not remember when his anxiety started but his headaches dated from when he was 19 and had an accident when cycling to work. We started work on his anxiety and, when relaxed, he continually recalled the time when he came off his bike and crashed head-first into a door. This was very early in the morning when there was nobody about to help him. He couldn't get up, his head was bleeding, he tried to call out and to bang on the door but nobody came to help him for hours and he lay on the cold, wet road until daylight. He spent three weeks in hospital as a result of that accident and I feel that we could certainly call that a traumatic event.

However, neither he nor I could see how he had created his anxiety nor his headaches as a result of that accident. The logical progression was missing. Then, finally, after another 3 sessions he remembered when he was 9 years old he used to wet the bed and his mother said she couldn't afford the continual laundry bills. At the following treatment he remembered being told by his father that he was giving his mother a lot of extra work and that they would have to exchange him for another boy if he kept on wetting his bed. Thereafter he used to get up before his mother in the morning to put his sheets and pyjamas in the airing cupboard to dry before she found them.

His anxiety, his desire to be ahead of himself, to be ridiculously early for work stemmed from this need to be up long before his mother so that everything was dry and she would never know he still wet the bed.

On the day, years later, when he had his accident he was unable to allay his anxiety by getting to work early and he coupled the pain of his head injury with this fact to create continual head pains and increase his anxiety.

There was no doubt that the accident was the most traumatic event of his life and we had considerable trouble in getting to the true cause. This was not really traumatic as, even before his parents used the words that 'loaded his gun', he had known they were both very unhappy about his bed-wetting problem and by getting up early he had overcome his fear of being traded-in for a non-bedwetter.

Yet the wet-sheet threat was the real cause of his problem. If that had never happened he would not have suffered anxiety and without that need to get to work early being thwarted by his accident he would not have experienced his headaches. Once again the really traumatic incident was not the true cause of the problem and to have dealt with the worst incident – the accident – would still have left his anxiety untouched to show itself in what may have been a totally different way.

If I had just worked on the 'trigger', the accident – the real trauma, I could probably have allayed his anxiety for a time and almost certainly got rid of his headaches; but the real cause of his problem would have been left untouched. So what happens when there is a bus strike (he no longer cycled to work) or there is thick snow which prevents him getting to work on time?

He would be unable to 'get ahead of himself' so his anxiety would probably return. Maybe his headaches would come back. Maybe he develops insomnia from a fear of wetting himself while asleep. Possibly he becomes even more anxious about getting to work early to such an extent that on one of the days that he drives he goes too fast and causes his own or another person's death.

Many therapists will content themselves with uncovering a traumatic event while a Curative Hypnotherapist will find out WHY he reacted to that event in the way that he did.

JANE had a fear of heights. She was also a member of one of my training courses a few years ago who volunteered to have treatment while on the course. Her husband liked walking up mountains at the weekends and she admitted that she used to keep her boots in one place, her gloves in another and her headgear in a third place so that it took as long as possible for her to get ready to accompany him. At the consultation she said she knew this was silly but she couldn't help it.

The first incident she recalled was the the worst one without any doubt. She remembered standing on the ground looking up at her son leaning over the ramparts of a castle. She was terrified that he would fall but was even more terrified when someone came up behind him and took him away from the edge and out of the sight of Jane. She went to look for him but couldn't find him. She searched the castle for half an hour, getting more and more upset, before eventually being reunited with him.

Once again there was no logicality to her developement of a fear of heights as a result of this incident, so we tried again and went to a scene in the circus when she was 6 years old. She saw a trapeze artist fall from high up in the big-top and was scared, not realising that it was a common trick where the girl was attached to the trapeze or another high support by a rope around her ankle, and her fall was stopped before she hit the ground.

At a circus there is certain to be a large number of children who all saw the same thing happen. So, we have to ask whether all those kids developed a fear of heights as a result of what they witnessed. Naturally, the answer is "no" which means that Jane was reacting to something else that had happened. So we tried again.

The real incident that caused her problem was the death of her father when she was very young. Her mother had to put her into the care of a convent and on the way into the building her mother pointed up to the sky and told her that her father was 'up there'. In simple terms her problem was caused by the childish association of heights and death yet, her mother's words were in no way traumatic at all – she already knew that her father was dead and had known for several days that she was going to leave her mother and go to the convent – in fact she was quite looking forward to the new experience and there was no trauma, no unwelcome emotion whatsoever involved in the true incident that lay at the very root of the problem.

A traumatic happening can occasionally cause a problem but, more usually, it is only the trigger and a good therapist will find out why the patient is reacting to that event by creation of a symptom. In the investigation the therapist should be able to uncover not just the incident itself but the patients interpretation of what took place.

It is that interpretation which is the key. It is not what happens that creates a problem but the way it is interpreted by the individual. The less important an event, the more likely a person is to accept first impressions, and the less likely they are to take the trouble to analyse what has happened. Therefore, the less traumatic an event the more likely it is to be misinterpreted.

The more traumatic an incident may be, the more it will be analysed, but that analysis has to be done in the light of previous experience. When we look at incidents we bring to bear all previous happenings that could influence our reactions – including our beliefs, our mis-understanding, our mis-interpretations.

Usually wrong information is simply the result of a mis-interpretation. Following the linguist Noam Chomsky, Keith Oatly, in his book 'Brain Mechanisms and Mind' (Thames and Hudson) asks us to consider the following sentence:

FLYING PLANES CAN BE DANGEROUS

Mr. Oatly points out: "This single order of words can have either of two meanings which can be loosely paraphrased as follows:

a) piloting planes can be a dangerous occupation

OR

b) planes flying around can be dangerous to people nearby."

If someone uses the phrase quoted they have a definite meaning in their mind so, whatever meaning you put on those words has a 50% chance of being wrong and your interpretation will have been made in accordance with whatever previous information you may have absorbed.

After all the decades that have passed I can still remember my shock the first time I was able to read the words 'Family Butcher' over a shop, but I had understanding by the time I came across the sign 'High Class Family Butcher' although I still smile to myself as I imagine a line of Earls, resplendent in coronets and ermine, waiting to be beheaded.

Mine was a simple mis-interpretation which has had no effect on me (or so I believe), but other misunderstandings can be just as simple yet cause genuine and very distressing problems.

An interesting thought on 'interpretation': A school teacher's problem was caused by her headmaster giving her a bad reference for a new job because he considered her racist. He accused her of not being fair to the West Indian children in her class and pointed out to her that they were more volatile and she must make allowances for this. She took the attitude that it is wrong to discriminate on the grounds of colour or race, and that all her pupils should conform to the same standards of behaviour. She said that she would not allow disruptive behaviour by white children and her ethics would not permit her to treat black ones any differently.

Would you consider that she was racist because she would not make special allowance for the West Indians? Would you consider that the headmaster was racist in wanting her to treat blacks differently to whites? Were both of them racist – or neither? What is your interpretation?

When a mother says to her child "go away", does she mean:

'leave me alone for a few moments while I concentrate'

OR

'I never want to see you again'

OR

'get out of the kitchen quickly as I think the gas stove is going to blow up and I want you safe and out of harm'

Does it mean love or hate? Does it show concern for safety or rejection?

The actual meaning is not important in the creation of the childs reaction. The important thing is the way the child interprets those two simple words. Their future reactions will be based on that understanding.

The child who hears those words addressed to her (I'll decide it is a girl and her name is Alice) brings into instant play everything to do with the person who uttered the words, the circumstances (as Alice understands them) in which they are spoken, the facial expression that accompanied them, the tone of voice and her previous experience of the individual words themselves.

All these aspects and many others are used to make an interpretation. And it is that interpretation that is accepted, whether for good or ill.

I have taken a simple incident apparently consisting of just two words – "Go away". How can such a silly happening create a problem? and what sort of problem?

Assume Alice wanted to share something with her mother when she was rebuffed. Would she decide not to share in the future and become secretive?

Would she develop jealousy for her sister, Martha, whom she had never heard treated in this way?

Would she develop a lack of confidence because of implied criticism when she was doing nothing wrong?

Would she become overweight as a result of rejection (see the book 'Hypnotherapy Explained')?

Remember that one thing builds on top of another. Once a programme has been started in her computer, it will add to that programme any other thing that occurs that may SEEM relevant.

Let us take the second assumption. Alice has never heard Martha treated like this. When her next birthday comes round she is given a present by her mother which, although it may be very expensive, she does not think is as nice as the one given to Martha on her birthday. If the above incident had not taken place, she would probably have accepted the present and hope for a better deal next time. But this incident HAS happened and therefore she knows why she has an inferior present. It is because her mother rejects her.

It is confirmation of that rejection, thus when a further incident takes place she has two incidents of maternal rejection to which her computer refers when making an interpretation and the feeling grows bigger and bigger. All the time the problem feeds on itself – and all caused by two carelessly spoken words when her mother was frustrated because her poor eyesight made it difficult for her to thread a needle (or something equally insignificant).

Obviously I have made up the details of Alice and her family but my point is that in the vast majority of cases the incident that lies at the root of a person's problem is something that, in isolation, appears completely unimportant.

It is very rare that important or traumatic events create problems. If something really important takes place one looks at it, one analyses before letting it past the conscious mind into the part that reacts. The things that slip past the analytical part of your mind are the things that are not worthwhile analysing at the time they took place. However, once they are in the sub-conscious they have just as much validity as the incidents that have been analysed and will play the same part in causing reactions.

In 1987 the periodical "Chat" had a story about a lady who had been to a hypnotherapist to see if he could stop her nightmares and the report described the incident which had 'started' her problem. Apparently she had been on a pier at the seaside as a child and petrol had been poured on the sea then ignited and an escapologist who was already bound in chains and a straight-jacket had been thrown into the middle of the flames. This was stated to be the incident that caused her problem but do YOU really think that every child who witnessed this event developed nightmares? Is this not the sort of event that helps to really make a holiday for a child – something exciting for them to talk about when they get back to school?

If other kids do not develop nightmares then there has to be something else in the mind of the one that does. She has to be reacting to something else for her to carry the symptom of nightmares with her a quarter of a century later when she is an adult and has known for years that this was just an escapologist's stunt and there was no harm or damage done to him.

Unfortunately the publication called this therapist a "Curative" Hypnotherapist whereas the treatment as described was most certainly not curative. To cure you have to find out – and then correct – the cause; but all that had been done in this case was to deal with the trigger. This lady's gun is still loaded and she stands a very good chance of another trigger creating a problem for her in the future.

When undergoing Hypnotherapy every patient should ask themselves whether the therapist is trying to persuade them that a particular event is the cause of their problem or whether the information on the true incident comes from the patient themselves. They should question themselves as to whether the majority of people in similar circumstances would react in the same way as they have, and if the answer is 'NO', then the therapist should have the ability to find out, from the patient, WHY they had this incorrect reaction.

A perfect example of non-traumatic events causing a serious problem was a man who had suffered very severe headaches for over 40 years. When a young lad of 4, his mother told him to come away from a drain as it contained germs and "they'll get into your head". (No trauma there).

When in hypnosis he had difficulty in recalling precisely why and how he had created these continually recurring headaches because "it filled me with a greater fear than I had ever known".

At 11, when watching a drain being cleaned out, his mother again told him to keep away from this fascinating operation with similar comments about germs. (Still no trauma).

A short while thereafter he was ill with scarlet fever. (discomfort but no trauma).

Then he made the connection between his mothers' original words about germs getting into his head and his illness, and brought into play a third factor. "It was 1940, the beginning of World War Two. There were propaganda posters about informing us that 'coughs and sneezes spread diseases'. Germs were allies of the enemy and even part of the name 'GERMan'. Pictures of germs were shown looking like evil tadpoles. They had viscious teeth, a small black moustache and even had a swastika armband on. These were my germs. They could eat their way into your brain and give you terrible headaches."

"Now I was programmed".

This patient was treated on a training course of which he was a member. All except the final part of his treatment was witnessed by the rest of those in training. Brian Godfrey is now in practice as a Curative Hypnotherapist in Portishead, Avon. He knows only too well how his imagination created for him "hell without the comfort of a warm fire", and how a full understanding enabled him to cure himself.

Brian wrote up his case for the Hypnotherapy Journal (Association of Qualified Curative Hypnotherapists) and said: "Needless to say, when the cause was found under hypnosis, I thought 'how stupid' and eventually laughed. Every time I had been ill there had been such severe headaches that I had been diagnosed, on various occasions, as having meningitis, migraine, possible brain tumour, stroke or haemorrhage. On one occasion, when in hospital, they thought I had died on them for a while and came round just prior to having the shock equipment applied".

Just imagine if Brian had visited a hypnotherapist who tried suppressing his headaches or one who tried to get him to fit the therapists' own particular theory. He would be left with this huge, viscious, black germ still chomping away at his brain with its massive teeth and creating troubles at which we can only guess.

It is impossible to cure anything without finding out the CAUSE. Many people will finish treatment by hypnosis believing that they have been cured – because the therapist has said so. They believe the therapist. After all, they went to him in the first place because they thought him to be an expert. If you are told and believe that your fear of driving (for example) has gone, then there will obviously be a decrease in the phobia itself – I just hope that I am not on the same motorway as you when something triggers your problem again!

The Sexual Element

Picture this scene: The patient, a man, beautifully relaxed in the consulting room, the Hypnotherapist commencing the questioning:–

Therapist: "Do you have any problems with personal relationships?"

Patient: "No."

Therapist: "Do you have any sexual problems?"

Patient: "No."

Therapist: "So you enjoy sex fully, do you?"

Patient: "Yes."

Therapist: "Do you enjoy the sight of a woman with a good figure?"

Patient: "Yes."

Therapist: "A woman's breasts are an essential part of their appearance, aren't they?"

Patient: "Yes."

Therapist: "So you enjoy the sight of a woman's breasts, do you?"

Patient: "Yes."

Therapist: "Do you like touching them?"

Patient: "Yes."

Therapist: "When you are walking down the street and see a woman with an attractive figure do you ever have the feeling that you would like to touch her breasts?"

Patient: "Yes."

The above imaginary scene shows a not very sophisticated method of questioning which will easily let the therapist lead a patient towards a problem that they never really had and it is probably something like this which accounts for the headline **"CASE OF THE BOOB GRABBERS"** which appeared in "The People" newspaper in 1986 or '87 with a sub-headline of **"JUDY TREATS SEX FREAKS"**. The article that followed stated that one of the most common complaints that this hypnotist treats "is men with an irresistible urge to grab women's boobs in the street".

"Believe it or not I'm treating more than a dozen boob-grabbers at the moment" this lady is reported as saying and the story goes on to say that she admits that she doesn't know either the cause or the cure of this strange 'phobia'.

Leaving aside the fact that anyone with this problem does not have a 'phobia' (which means a 'fear'), any proper Hypnotherapist should start questioning their own feelings and motives if they have such a high number of people with an unusual compulsion such as this newspaper report states. In all the years I have been practicing I have treated many men and women with all types of unusual and sometime bizarre sexual desires but I have never had a 'boob-grabber' who presented this as their problem at the consultation.

The therapist in question may feel that her views were not fully represented by the newspaper, but from the case as it is described it seems to be, that to have this many patients all at one time with a peculiar compulsion and not to be able to find out the cause in a single case, means that this lady can have little idea of the correct use of hypnosis, and one is also forced to the conclusion that she is leading her patient – perhaps consciously to get 'kicks' – perhaps sub-consciously because of her own particular kink or sexual hang-up about her own or other women's breasts.

It is unbelievably easy to lead a person whether under hypnosis or not. Just imagine if the first answer given by the patient at the beginning of this chapter had been a "yes" instead of a "no". No patient can win against a therapist who has a pre-conceived idea of what is causing their problem and the most important point I am always having to stress on the first few days of my training courses is that the patient, and only the patient, knows how they have interpreted events to create their problem. To try to make them fit the therapists' ideas does them no good in the long run. It is therapist's job to find out FROM THE PATIENT how and why they have created their problem. **The only way to cure is to find the cause.**

Pre-conceived ideas of many sorts keep cropping up in many training schools, even in those who claim to cure. One comes across theories such as a fear of dentists meaning that the person has a castration complex although how this ties in with, for instance, a female patient of mine who during treatment recalled, when she was 3 years old, her mother returning from the dentist and saying "he nearly killed me". A simple exaggeration that was accepted uncritically by a young child and created the fear that she could be killed if she went for treatment. As simple as the acceptance of a young boy whose father said "they're butchers" in similar circumstances.

There are far too many therapists who will attempt to force their theories onto their patients and the teacher who believes the above theory, also talks about letting a patient produce random memories until they come up with something sexual, then works on this aspect – a pre-conceived idea if ever I heard one. He also accuses his patients of having a 'guilty secret' without making any attempt to find out whether guilt really lies at the root of the problem – it could just as easily be embarrassment, or anger, or jealousy, or any other emotion.

To try to make a patient fit the therapist's theory does them little good; the poor man in the 'boob-grabbing' report at the start of this chapter now believes he has some sort of sex problem and this belief could create an actual sex problem in the future and will certainly cause some considerable confusion.

This unfortunate man has now been given a problem by the therapist which should mean it is nice and easy for her to correct it. But therapists who are so ignorant of the use of hypnosis that they will create problems in this way are highly unlikely to have the ability to correct them. If she had that ability she would have used it on the original problem – and we don't even know what that was, and the therapist was not bothered about it at all.

I well remember one attractive girl who came for treatment with the problem of a consuming jealousy and was in a terribly confused state due to the fact that her previous therapist had been trying to convince her that her problem was caused by her desire to be a boy. If you could have seen her anger when she recalled her mother cutting off her "pretty curls" you couldn't have believed this for a second, but this therapist also had some sort of problem that she was bringing into treatment as other patients who had previously been to her for treatment have told me she was continually talking about how all the men she treated got erections while in relaxation.

This leads straight to an article I wrote for the Hypnotherapy Journal (Association of Qualified Curative Hypnotherapists) of July 1985 (and I make no apology for repeating for a wider audience the words I originally intended for Hypnotherapists – I also do so elsewhere in this book).

In this article I quoted from the editorial of the British Journal of Clinical Hypnosis (July-Oct 1973) which gave the following 'reason' why only a qualified psychiatrist should use Hypnosis:

> "some years ago, a prominemt American psychiatrist
> described how many of his female patients experienced

orgasm during the trance state, and on these grounds
advocated that no-one except a qualified
psychiatrist should practice Hypnotherapy"

The writer of the editorial (also a psychiatrist) went on to say that:

"Neither I nor most of my psychiatric colleagues have ever seen
this happen"

and the use of the word "most" presumably means that some of them
have seen this phenomenon – otherwise why bother to put it forward as
a serious point?

Any person who uses hypnosis, whether as a serious professional
therapist, an amateur or an entertainer, knows that their female
patients will NOT experience an orgasm unless they have that
intention before hypnosis or unless the therapist deliberately leads
them into it – and in that case **they still have to be willing to follow his
lead.**

One has to query:

Why does this only happen to females?

Who has the problem – the patient or the therapist?

Is the suggestion being made that only psychiatrists should be
allowed to help a woman achieve orgasm which, presumably,
rules out sexual activity by every other heterosexual male and
lesbian.

This is a perfect example of a 'therapist' giving themselves therapy at
the expense of the patient. It is obvious that if therapists need this sort
of experience then they have a sexual problem and, if they cannot stop
it intruding into the treatment of people who need genuine help, they
should not be involved in treating others.

Like the lady with the boob-grabbers, the man who lets a patient
ramble on until they come up with something sexual then works on this
aspect, and the lady whose male patients all get erections, the
psychiatrist whose female patients experience orgasm obviously feel a
need to indulge their own fantasies and do a great disservice to genuine
Hypnotherapists.

Do not get the idea that I am saying that Hypnotherapists are perfect
and have no problems. I know of none like that. Problems or hang-ups
do not prevent a therapist doing a first class job with their patients – as
long as they do not allow them to intrude into treatment.

Sex plays its' part in creating problems but no more so than a feeling of inadequacy, rejection, anger, jealousy, shame, fear or any other emotion and to attempt to make a patient fit the therapists' theories can be a very damaging procedure.

From another article in the same issue of the Journal of Clinical Hypnosis comes the case reported by a dentist who was having difficulty getting some ladies to put dentures in their mouth because of their inclination to feel sick when he attempted to insert them. With a large number of patients he found useful what he called a 'sick stick' – a broom handle or an inch-thick piece of polished copper piping for them to concentrate on. He goes on to say: "A Freudian psychologist friend of mine agreed in principle with the sick-stick and said there could be nothing better than a 2-foot-long rigid phallic symbol to grip hard on".

Once again our common-sense makes us ask:

1 Would a man respond to gripping a 'rigid phallic symbol' belonging to someone else in the same way as a woman responds?

2 How would a lesbian respond?

3 If a heterosexual woman transfers her revulsion for her new teeth to the broom handle and the handle represents a penis, does it not seem obvious that the sequel will be a dislike of normal sexual intercourse?

In reality, this dentist was simply getting the lady to concentrate on something other than what he was doing, and these people with their sexual obsessions create considerable apprehension in potential hypnotherapy patients, making the commencement of treatment more difficult and, I am sure, preventing some people coming for treatment which would benefit them.

The British Journal of Clinical Hypnosis was published by the British Society of Medical and Dental Hypnosis which is a body whose membership is confined to Doctors and Dentists, and I find it very disturbing that people whose main jobs are outside hypnosis are trying to control the activities of professional Hypnotherapists. They do not have the experience or understanding to be allowed to do so.

To quote from my personal experience: some years ago I thought that I needed some help with my tension and felt that I might be too critical or analytical if I went to one of the people I had trained. I therefore went to a Doctor who practices Hypnotherapy. At the consultation the vast majority of his questions were not about my symptoms but about my sex-life. I had (and still have) no problems, hang-ups, obsessions, neuroses, or difficulties of any kind in this part of my life.

From this questioning it was obvious that he had pre-conceived ideas and his 'solution' to my problem was going to lie somewhere in the sexual field whether I liked it, believed it, accepted it, or not. His mind was made up, he wasn't going to find out, he already 'knew' and consequently, long before the treatment started, my confidence in him was virtually nil.

When he asked me what I did for a living and I told him I was a Hypnotherapist his response was "We don't agree with lay-people using Hypnosis".

"Who is the lay-man?" I replied, "You are a full time Doctor who does a little hypnotherapy on the side, whereas I do well over 6O hours of Hypnotherapy every week".

It was obvious that our relationship was not on a very good footing from the start but I still wanted, and was prepared to accept treatment but, maybe because he thought I was there to criticise him, he was far too off-hand to enable me to accept his feeble efforts to induce hypnosis. He gave it just a cursory few minutes then sat back in his chair with an exasperated sigh and said "You're suffering from depression. I'll send a note to your Doctor for him to give you some pills".

I didn't have the heart to tell the poor man that a high percentage of the people who come to me for treatment have been suffering from depression and in many cases have been on pills for years. Quite a number of them have been recommended by their Doctor to come to me to see if I could help them come off anti-depressants or tranquilisers.

While I am certainly not successful in every case, I have too much concern for the people who visit me to suggest they go to their doctor for pills without first really trying hard to cure their problem. Pills may help their symptoms – or may not. Many people get 'hooked' and the Daily News (l3th.Feb/87) reported that 92,880 people in the West Midland region alone had been on these drugs for more than seven years, yet the same article reports doctors as saying that the physical effects wear off after only four months!

Wouldn't you feel 'depressed' if you went for help with mild tension and ended up being told that you should take mind-bending drugs for depression?

Wouldn't you feel 'depressed' if, as a skilled person in your field, you found someone who plays at your craft, and badly at that, yet not only considers themselves as good as you, but even better because of their skill in another therapy which has no connection with your own?

At the end of this interview I admit I felt depressed – but that was a natural reaction, not the unnatural reaction of suffering from 'Depression'.

He obviously felt that I threatened his status as a doctor and was certainly allowing this problem to intrude into treatment.

Can we really call these people Hypnotherapists with a proper understanding of the power of Hypnosis?

I shudder to think how many other people may have gone to this man for help, have not accepted his first attempt to induce hypnosis, and been told that they are suffering from depression. How many of them, believing him to be an expert, accept his diagnosis and have ended up on pills or even imagining that they have depression and creating the symptoms.

I also shudder when I think of how his obvious emphasis on sex could lead people into believing that there is something abnormal about themselves and developing real problems in this area.

Sexual abuse of children has recently featured prominently in the news and there is, in fact, so much emphasis on it that it appears there are people who will find it where it does not exist. But worse than this is the effect on those who come to believe that they were abused, and the innocent who are accused and sometimes convicted of abuse due to this publicity.

A recent case was a lady of 37 who told me at the consultation of how, when she was seven years old, she was talking to a man she knew who was sitting on the grass in the park and who said to her "put your hand in my pocket and you'll find some sweets". She had put her hand in his trouser pocket and "there were no sweets – I felt his private parts".

She thought that this was the reason why she could not bear touching her husband sexually or being touched in any way at all even by one of her own daughters whose ages ranged from 12 down to 1½ years.

But the real reason for her problem was: "He was angry. He shouted at me. He told me off for touching him there. I didn't know what to do. I knew it was wrong. I felt it. *I thought he'd tell mum*".

The fear that he would tell her mother was at the root of her problem. The actual touching caused no problem, which was created by the fear of other people's reactions to the incident. In fact it was possible that the man was completely genuine as between them on the grass lay his jacket with one of the pockets uppermost. Obviously, we shall never know what this man's true intention was; but the lady started her treatment believing that this was sexual abuse. She remembered the incident but had wiped out of her conscious mind the words that caused the fear that the fault was hers.

Another incident in a park springs into my mind – a woman who said she was sexually abused by her grandfather. During treatment the truth came out. She had run towards her grandfather who was sitting on a park bench, climbed onto the seat and put her arms round him and gave him a hug. He put his arm around her and, because of the height she was when standing on the seat, his hand went underneath her very short skirt onto the back of her knickers.

Some time later her mother told her that she must not let a man touch her "near her bottom" and this created a feeling that there was something wrong with her because she had experienced a pleasurable feeling while being touched there.

The feeling of pleasure actually came from the hugging but she believed, until she recalled all the details under hypnosis, that she had been anally assaulted.

Genuine abuse of children, whether sexual or not, is one of the most repulsive things of which I can conceive but the current publicity is making people believe, genuinely believe, there has been abuse when none really exists. Is it really worse for a child to be sexually touched, **without threats or violence,** than to pull a pan of boiling water off the stove and scald themselves? Is it worse, **if no pain or threats of any sort are involved,** for a child to touch another person sexually than to be mangled in a car accident or to be savaged by a dog?

Of course it is not. A child has natural curiosity and experiences sexual feelings even though these feelings may be immature. These things are a part of normal life – the abnormality comes from the reactions of others. The guilt, shame, embarrassment or other emotion with which these experiences are overlaid is not natural to children but 'educated' into them, and guilt about childish sexual feelings is probably the biggest cause of problems which are found to be based on a sexual incident.

Both sexes demonstrate that they experience sexual pleasure from early babyhood right up to the time that they are taught that it is wrong. They may then sub-consciously try to find a scapegoat upon whom to place the blame as is often demonstrated during treatment. The two letters quoted in chapter 11 demonstrate how a person will create a fantasy to cover up feelings of guilt, shame or embarrassment even though these are the emotions of a child.

These same emotions lie at the root of the general attitude of the media in their handling of sexual abuse of children. It is, for instance, not really accepted that women indulge in this as well as men. An example was a full page article in the Daily News (21.Jan.1986) illustrated with two large drawings of a man sitting on a bed in which lay a little girl. A whole page with just a tiny paragraph at the very end stating "Her research (Diane Core) shows that it is no longer usually stepfathers and live-in lovers who abuse children in the home. Just as many women abuse their sons". Experience in practice would force me to add "and daughters".

Yet the cases of women sexually abusing children do not get anything like the same prominence as those involving men thus perpetuating the belief in many patients that is a male perversion and creating greater problems because the individuals will not accept the truth when they recall it and, in therapy, cover up the unacceptable.

If a headmaster of a school was accused of indecently assaulting girls of 10 and 11, this would almost certainly have made headlines not just the tiny mention in the Birmingham Mail of 6th.March '87 devoted to a headmistress.

The Daily Mirror of 25th.Nov.1986 gave little more space to a 16-year-old girl who stripped a 9-year-old boy then undressed herself and sexually assaulted him.

The Sunday Times 19/8/84 & 25/11/84 quotes cases of female abusers but says that they are mostly in professions connected with children; teachers, social workers, etc., and amongst these cases is one of seven teachers, six of whom were women. A further case of a group of eight men and eight women who abused more than two dozen children is also quoted but this is still a more or less unacceptable concept to most people and they therefore change facts to fit their media-and-parent-programmed pre-conceived ideas when we are seeking the truth during treatment.

On July 17th.1989 there was broadcast a television investigation into 'Satanism' in which all types of sexual abuse of children was apparently uncovered. It was alleged that one 13-year-old girl was forced to become pregnant, then the foetus was aborted and ritually sacrificed. One of the leaders of the sect that carried out this horrific deed was said to be the teenager's own grandmother!

No-one has any reliable figures as to the ratio between men and women who are involved in 'occult' activities but I would feel safe in hazarding a guess that there are a lot more witches than there are warlocks. I have, over the years, had three ladies for treatment who said they were witches. All of them claimed to be 'white witches' but all agreed that sex, of one sort or another, played a large part in the rituals of their covens.

Even the law can add to the difficulties. A girl of 11 "lured a man into committing a sex act" because she wanted him to buy her a new colouring book. I appreciate that he was an adult and should have resisted what the Judge called "severe temptation" but he was jailed for 6 months while the girl, who deliberately set out to use sex to achieve her aim, was unpunished. (Evening Mail 28/3/87).

An unbelievably ridiculous travesty of Justice was reported by Phillip Knightley in the Sunday Times: In Brisbane, Australia, some women got drunk and tore the last stitch of clothing off a male stripper leaving him completely naked while "ringed fingers did unmentionable things to him".

Had the stripper been female, then a male audience would have been charged with indecent assault. However, as it was a female audience the male stripper was arrested and charged with indecent exposure for which he was convicted and fined! Even the Judiciary has the pre-conceived idea that the man has to be the guilty party!

In October 1979 the same newspaper quoted the results of a Mori poll which found out that babysitters, who are generally female, were responsible for 2 out of every 100 cases of sexual abuse and female strangers for a further two out of a hundred. Out of a total of over two thousand adults interviewed, 19 considered they had suffered permanent damage and a further 7 said that the quality of their life had been **improved** by the experience.

Sisters were mentioned as being culprits but there was no mention of mothers. Whether this was because the idea was unacceptable to the interviewers who formulated the questions or whether those interviewed were not prepared to admit to the true abuser, it does transpire, during therapy, that in a percentage of cases the patient recalls their mother using their sons and daughters to indulge their sexual feelings.

One has to bear in mind how a patient will cover up whatever is unpalatable to them, and will actually believe something that is more acceptable than the truth. It is more acceptable to be abused by a man, but the truth (which can never be accurately established) would show figures of female abusers being appreciably higher than those quoted.

Pre-conceived ideas absorbed by the patients create delays in effecting a cure. There is always a pre-disposition towards the attitude that 'my mother would never say, or do, anything to harm me'. Thus even if a patient is near recalling the truth their sub-conscious may be unwilling to remember the actual facts.

Usually, however, during the process of enabling a person to understand WHY they have created their problem, the truth is recalled. But imagine the outcome of treatment where the therapist does not understand Curative methods or is one of those with pre-conceived ideas and these revolve around everything being caused by a sexual incident and that the act must have been done by a man.

What terrible confusion would be created as their conscious mind blames one person while their sub-conscious knows that this is a lie.

The purpose of the last couple of pages has been to, hopefully, persuade those who come for therapy to put aside their beliefs as to the cause of their complaint. Most problems are not caused by a sexual incident and those that are could just as easily be created by a remark made about two dogs doing what comes completely naturally, which the hearer carries forward to a normal sexual experience or refers back to a normal bit of sexual exploration that may have taken place in childhood or it could be caused by something still far more innocent such as words to a child about an isolated incident of loss of bladder control due to excitement or even illness.

Of course sexual abuse of children takes place. It is done by males and females of all ages to both boys and girls. But if it takes place without any physical hurt or threat of harm then any problems that are caused by it are created by the attitude of society and the adults who influence the child.

All of us have gone through some sort of sexual incidents whether something heard, seen or felt long before we reach puberty. The girl who is bounced on her fathers knee and gets a pleasant feeling in between her legs has not been abused. But the current climate of publicity on the subject can make her believe that there is something peculiar about her as she should not allow her father to create those feelings; and there is only one person she can blame.

This publicity is the reason that the last few years has seen an increase in the people who say, at their consultation "I was a victim of incest" or "I was sexually abused as a child". It is not my job to try to find the truth of these statements but it usually transpires that, whatever their problem may be, it has nothing to do with the childish sexual event to which they are alluding. If such an incident does play a part in the creation of a problem then this is normally because of the attitude of another person. And remember that it is the patient who comes out with the true facts.

Sex with children is abhorrent. Sex with anyone who isn't willing is revolting but, just as a woman may be willing to have sex then feel guilty and cry 'rape' and eventually come to believe (in her conscious mind) that she was forced, so a child will create a fantasy even more easily and, because it is so much in the news, some children will actually use sexual blackmail as did the girl above who wanted a colouring book or the teacher who was eventually released from jail when the 11-year-old girl he was accused of molesting boasted to her friends that she was creating trouble for him because of the low marks he had given her (Sunday Times 19/8/84).

No good therapist will accept even a partial explanation of the event that is causing a problem if given from the conscious mind. They will start at the beginning and will find out, if not what actually happened, at least the interpretation of that event made by their patient.

Of course sexual incidents play their part in creating problems just as do incidents of rejection (whether real or imaginary) or events that cause jealousy, embarrassment or a feeling of inadequacy. **However, it is not what happens that creates a problem but the interpretation that the patient makes;** and this interpretation is made in accordance with what has already been learned and may, possibly, be altered in the light of future teachings.

Since the days of Freud, the emphasis on a sexual event being at the basis of all sorts of problems has prevented many people from seeking therapy and has created difficulties in finding out the truth from those who do attend for treatment. The publicity over the past few years about child sex abuse, and the assumption that it is always a man that is the abuser, has made the Curative Hypnotherapist's job even more difficult. But those engaged in our therapy can still win so long as they do not allow pre-conceived ideas, whether of themselves or their patients, to lead them away from the truth that lies in the mind of the person coming for help.

Let us turn to a less unpleasant aspect of the sexual beliefs. You are probably aware that:

> "people with light-coloured hair have less strands of hair growing per square inch than those with dark hair, and that red-heads have an even smaller quantity. As men with a full head of hair have a stronger sex-drive than those who are bald there is an obvious conclusion for the ladies to draw when chosing their mates."

Before I go any further may I ask you to consider the last paragraph once again as some of you reading it may have had experiences which lead them to disagree.

I disagree as well; and I have a perfect right to do so as I just dreamed up this fantasy.

I repeat it is untrue – but did you accept for a split-second? I am sure that if I put my mind to the task I could build this up into quite a theory but I put it here only to demonstrate the absurdity of some of the theories upon which people base their 'therapy'.

> "The female of the species, having no prominent external genitalia with which to make her sexuality obvious, feels subconsciously cheated or inferior. This is referred to as the castration complex. External features, such as the anterior teeth, are often symbolically substituted by the subconscious mind as alternatives. Thus, in certain patients, extraction of these teeth amounts to a major sexual assault and deprivation, and causes considerable emotional upset."

No, this is not another fantasy theory that I have concocted but is a quotation from an article written by a dentist, Mr.D.A.Hobbs, for the British Journal of Clinical Hypnosis (Oct.1969). (I am sure that you will have understood that 'the female of the species' means 'women' and that the 'anterior teeth' are the front teeth).

The author quotes un-named psychologists as originators of this theory but his following comments accept it uncritically and fully.

Yet I would have thought that women have a far more prominent feature than their teeth and, being a sexual 'prominence', one that is much more likely to be used as a 'penis substitute'. Even in these days of tight jeans, women have a much more prominent sexual feature than men – or rather two of them. I am right am I not? It is women who wear brassieres isn't it?

Of course women are upset when their front teeth are removed. It affects their appearance and even if they have them immediately replaced "by a prosthesis that is aesthetically more acceptable" these will not feel natural and there is the continual thought that others will become aware of the fact that she is wearing false teeth. I wonder why false teeth for women is not as acceptable as it is for men. Whatever the reason this is the cause of the "emotional upset". It has to do with general attractiveness not sex.

The ridiculous idea that most women suffer from 'penis envy" was once thought up. People without means of eliciting information from the sub-conscious accepted it and things have just built up from there. Unfounded theory upon unfounded theory. It makes those expounding the theories appear very learned but they are all built on nothing and make genuine therapy much more difficult as more and more patients hear of them and come for treatment with pre-conceived ideas in their conscious minds which makes the truth less acceptable and thus harder to uncover.

From the same article by this dentist comes the following quotation which is not on the sexual theme but is important in the context of unfounded statements that are made and then accepted by others without thought. In this article he states as a fact:

"We are born with only two instinctive fears: the fear of falling and the fear of loud noise. Apart from these two, all other fears are learned."

Many of us who have watched a child laughing while one of its parents pushes it higher and higher on a swing, would not have the nerve to shout "more" as the child is likely to. We would have learned a fear of falling, of heights.

Those of us who have thrown a baby into the air, caught it and heard its chortles of glee could not believe for one second that a person is born with a fear of falling; but that baby may grow up to develop a real dread of going more than three steps up a ladder - which is not nearly as high as they have been tossed when a baby.

"Come away from the edge" shouts the parent as the child wanders towards the edge of the cliff without any fears whatsoever. Fear of falling and fear of heights is very definitely learned and is not inborn yet this upside-down thinking results in the next sentence from this author: "One of the first fears to be learned is the fear of being harmed . . . " This truly is inborn. It is instinctive to avoid harm to oneself and the whole of our 'flight or fight' response is based on it. The whole purpose of our sub-conscious is personal survival whether physical, emotional or mental. This is not something that we learn.

I'll leave you to think about the theory as to whether we are born with a fear of loud noise and make just one final comment on the subject of sexual pre-conceived ideas: Some of the ladies who join our training courses believe that their 'feminine intuition' will be of assistance to them when treating people. One wrote on a section of the homestudy part of the course ". . . women therapists would use their intuition . . ."

When returning the paper I put on it the comment ". . . and men would back their hunches. Please explain the difference."

I have asked for enlightenment on this on numerous occasions. No one has yet even attempted an explanation.

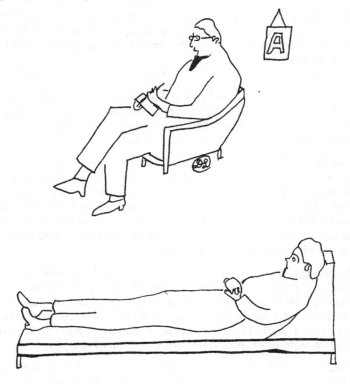

"My psychiatrist said it was a psecks problem"

Hypnosis – the Past, the Present and Things to Come

As I start this chapter I realise that it will almost certainly be the shortest one in this book.

This is partly because my only interest lies in the present and the future of Hypnotherapy and I have to admit to a glaring ignorance of the history of hypnosis, but then, how can you have a history of something that has never been defined?

Was it mass hypnosis that Hitler used or a straightforward appeal to the baser instincts of human beings and the promise of license to indulge them?

Was it hypno-anaesthesia when the first operation was performed: ". . . and the Lord God caused a deep sleep to fall upon Adam, and he slept: and He took one of his ribs, and closed up the place with flesh instead thereof"?

Genesis 2-21 (Authorised Version)

Were some of the miracles recorded in the Bible achieved through the use of hypnosis and are some of the miraculous cures that are still being recorded today nothing more than the acceptance of direct suggestion? And how long do a lot of these 'cures' last?

Accounts of "suggestive therapy" certainly go back as far as the ancient Greeks and there is an element of this in our modern medicine as is shown by properly controlled scientific tests of people with similar problems half of whom are given a genuine medicine and the other half a non-medicinal pill (a placebo) which they believe will alleviate their trouble – and in some of the latter cases there is an actual improvement – due purely to the power of suggestion.

500 years ago, magnets were passed over the body to induce a 'curative trance' and in the 18th century Anton Mesmer brought the power of direct suggestion to the notice of the world and, unfortunately, a lot of his methods and the mysticism involved are still in use to this day: To quote from Robert Darnton's book 'Mesmerism and the End of the Enlightenment in France' (Harvard University Press):

"Everything in Mesmer's indoor clinic was designed to produce a crisis in the patient. Heavy carpets, weird, astrological wall decorations, and drawn curtains shut him off from the outside world and muffled the occasional words, screams and bursts of hysterical laughter that broke the habitual heavy silence . . . Soft music, played on wind instruments, a pianoforte or glass harmonica . . . Every so often fellow patients collapsed, writhing on the floor . . ."

Does this remind you of ECT (electric shock treatment)? It is certainly very reminiscent of those therapists who still believe that patients must relive something traumatic and emotional, they must actually experience once again during therapy the terrible feelings which, to put it bluntly, may have nothing to do with the problem they wish to have treated. Some people do not seem able to move forward after two hundred years – or is it more than two thousand years? The above certainly reminds me of the 'casting out of devils'.

Thankfully more and more therapists who use hypnosis are moving on from this sadistic type of treatment with the understanding of how or, more importantly, WHY we create problems for ourselves because **it is only in understanding that cures can be found.**

Much of this book is on the subject of how hypnosis is now being used by the comparatively small, but steadily growing, number of Curative Hypnotherapists so I will not dwell on the present except to say that since the establishment of an INDEPENDENT examination body in 1983 (see appendix i) and the formation, 2 years later, of a Registered Charity (see appendix ii) to educate and promote the understanding of how to use hypnosis to CURE, there has been a steady increase in its acceptance.

So we turn to the future. A future which could see everything that has been built in the past shattered into meaningless fragments or a future of tremendous strides in the alleviation and cure of countless complaints suffered by millions of people.

We are beseiged by the trade union of the orthodox medical profession who believe that all therapy should be in the hands of doctors of medicine whose training is long and thorough but appears to blind them to the possibility of cure and whose understanding of hypnosis is very slight indeed.

We are, or may be, up against the might of the European Parliament whose 'harmonisation of laws' throughout the Common Market could make the practice of hypnotherapy subservient to the medical profession or insist that every hypnotherapist is medically qualified. Virtually all those who have come on my training courses are mature adults with a living to earn and families to support. They are not in a position to do seven years full time training in a therapy which will have no bearing on the one that they will be qualified to follow.

However, I do not believe that the picture is black. We have been assured that those who have qualified through our course of training before the date of 'harmonisation' will be able to continue in practice and our course meets the future anticipated requirements. Popular support from the public is growing fast and if repressive laws are enacted they would create great difficulties in enforcement.

I cannot believe that any government would deliberately attempt to stifle progress in the way that is suggested by some scaremongers. I, in fact, believe that serious research will be started in Curative Hypnotherapy. Proper 'clinical' trials are the next step. A scientific measurement of results is a necessity – and it will come. It needs funding which we cannot afford at present. But it will come.

Curative Hypnotherapy is a therapy in its own right and cannot operate in a subordinate position to other therapies whether 'orthodox' medicine, other methods of using hypnosis or psychiatry.

Curative methods of hypnotherapy are the most logical move forward. They use the patients own logic to CORRECT THE CAUSE of symptoms. They are without side effects. The treatment is not unpleasant. The speed at which results can be obtained is almost unbelievable and, above all, **Curative Hypnotherapy is the only treatment which can actually CURE so many problems.**

Theories and Fallacies

On the first page of this book I used the expression that doctors appeared to feel that hypnosis threatens their status.

This is, of course, a generalisation. There are a small number of doctors who do not seem to have this fear and are prepared to talk about the power and use of hypnosis in a rational way. Even these, however, still appear to think in terms of using hypnosis to suppress symptoms, presumably because of their long years of training which makes it difficult for them to break out of the mental rut into which this education has forced them.

Let me hasten to say that I am not anti-medical. I would not like to think of being without the services of doctors whether in general practice or hospital. The services that doctors offer and the advances made in the medical and surgical fields enable untold millions of people to experience, at the very least, a reduction of their symptoms; but even those doctors who have seen results from the Curative use of hypnosis appear unable to accept that anything is achieved except relaxation and symptom suppression.

Time and again patients who have experienced complete cessation of symptoms, for which they have been medically treated for 20 years or more, following a couple of months of Curative Hypnotherapy are told by their doctors that this is 'natural remission'. What a fantastic coincidence that after being on drugs for year after year they lose their problem after six weeks or so of Curative Hypnotherapy! And what a further marvellous coincidence that this happens in case after case!

I feel that the fear of the medical profession is not so much of hypnosis itself, but the threat that non-medical people can cure (or even alleviate symptoms) when they cannot. It is a threat to their status. It is also a threat to the basis of their profession which, even though they pay lip-service to 'stress induced disease' they still try to treat with physical means. They know that stress has a mental origin but they still treat it with drugs that have to work through the physical systems of the body before they can have any effect on the mind.

Their biggest fear seems to be caused by the fact that virtually all good hypnotherapists appear to be non-medically trained although many nurses and one or two doctors and dental surgeons have been on my training courses and are now practicing as Curative Hypnotherapists. Some 'orthodox' medical people will recommend a hypnotherapist if it is a qualified doctor - even though this person may have no real understanding of hypnosis and uses it only a few hours every now and then. Apart from the very few doctors who have been on my own training courses, I have never heard of a doctor who puts the natural methods of hypnosis first and even those doctors who use hypnosis only appear to understand symptom suppression - leaving the cause of the problem untouched to create future trouble.

Doctors will normally only suggest hypnosis when all else has failed. What a pity they do not then recommend experts in this field, people who are professional Curative Hypnotherapists, who are totally dedicated to the use of hypnosis and are thus vastly more experienced in its use and have a far greater understanding of how it can be used to maximum and lasting advantage.

This attitude of most doctors is evidenced by writing like that of David Waxman (Hypnosis. A Guide for Patients and Practitioners — Balliere) who states several times that only a medically qualified person should be visited for hypnotherapy, without once giving a reason of any sort, and Hellmut Karle (Hypnosis and Hypnotherapy — Thorsons Publishers Ltd) (page 78) who writes that non-medically qualified hypnotherapist "lack the training, knowledge and experience", completely ignoring the fact that my training courses are longer and **far more thorough** than that given to members of the Society which he recommends, and that a full-time hypnotherapist MUST have more experience than a person who uses hypnosis occasionally without any real understanding. More importantly, he appears to be completely unaware that there is **more than one way to use hypnosis.**

Many people who use hypnosis in treatment have the most weird and wonderful theories. None of them, however, can tell you how these ideas evolved or show any proof of their validity. There are therapists who believe that all problems are caused as you travel down the birth canal; others who believe that homosexuality is caused by loss of the umbilical cord (have you checked yours recently?).

There are those who believe that every problem is created by something that made the sufferer feel guilt or has a sexual cause, and there are those who start off by categorising people into 'oral', 'anal' or 'genital' types. Caroline and David Shreeve, in their book "The Healing power of Hypnotism" (Thorsons Publishers) (para 3 page 60) actually make statements like "...I looked for an underlying cause in the oral stage of her development . . . ." Could one have a firmer pre-conceived idea than this? Yet everybody creates their problems through a completely individual, completely unique mental process as my patients have proved dozens of times over the years in public – when we work with people with genuine problems on training courses.

Although without any foundation that I can discover, this 'oral, anal, genital' classifying of people has a number of therapists who subscribe to it so it may be worth-while a little exploration in this book:–

In essence, the theory is that so-called 'oral' types have their main traits of character formed in the first three years of life; the 'anal' people during the next couple of years; and those who form their main traits between the age of 5 and puberty are known as 'genital' types.

'Oral' types are **supposed to be** introverted, self-centred and shy, while 'anal' types are paranoid, ruthless and jealous and 'genital' people are assumed to be shallow and immature.

The above are very brief descriptions as the point I wish to make is that it serves no purpose to categorise people in this way. Yet whole books have been written on the subject and complete training courses are based on this idea of fitting people into nice, neat compartments. Whether the patient likes it or not these therapists, teachers and writers will make them fit – but none of them have ever, to my knowledge, **demonstrated a CURE.**

This book does not contain a lot of actual case histories but as you read those that are included, or the case studies in my previous book, I would like you to think about whether the people described fit into these categories or not (bearing in mind that, according to this theory, everyone is either an 'oral', 'anal' or 'genital' type) and whether knowing their 'type' could be of any assistance in helping them to cure their arthritis, overcome their obesity or regain their confidence.

Unproven theories and pre-conceived ideas are the biggest stumbling blocks to actually curing a person of a problem. Time after time those of us who do Curative Hypnotherapy are proving that only the sufferer has the information as to how they have created their problem. Where does the mis-information lie in their computer? What is this wrong data that they have absorbed sometime in the past?

I have already written about how a computer has to work logically in accordance with the information in its memory banks and how a different sequence of the same events can produce differing answers and I would now like you to consider the following true case:

Under Hypnosis a lady with a weight problem recalled an occasion in her childhood when she did not feel hungry and refused to eat. Her father told her that if she did not eat properly she would "end up like Theresa next door".

The neighbour's daughter had tuberculosis, had become very thin, and died from the disease. Because of her father's comment the child – my patient – had taken the facts in the following order:

1. Theresa did not eat sufficiently THEREFORE:
2. She became thin THEREFORE:
3. She got tuberculosis THEREFORE:
4. She died.

My patient believed that Theresa has developed tuberculosis BECAUSE she had become thin and knew that people become thin if they do not eat sufficient food.

This was the sequence in which the information regarding Theresa had been presented to her and therefore it was the sequence in which she had absorbed it.

She then took a completely logical – although sub-conscious – decision not to become thin because if she lost sufficient weight she would get TB and then die. In fact she developed a margin for error in carrying around about 50lbs of excess weight!

This may seem a ridiculous reaction but remember my lady was only a child when she absorbed this information and, because she had forgotten the incident, was now unable to use her commonsense to correct it. To do this she would have to isolate the actual information with her conscious mind. She could not 'put her finger' on what was creating her problem. The details were only in her sub-conscious and her reaction was thus a completely logical one.

But let us now assume that she had absorbed those facts in a completely different order:

1. Theresa got tuberculosis THEREFORE:
2. She lost her desire for food THEREFORE:
3. She became thin THEREFORE:
4. She died

Now we have exactly the same facts but in a completely different sequence and when the truth came out during treatment and my patient realised why she had created her excessive weight, she also immediately realised that her reaction was wrong. She had, since that early incident, learnt that it was the disease that caused the wasting away and not the loss of weight that caused the disease. She was, therefore, able to lose her compulsion to overeat because this would not ward off the illness.

There is, of course, at least one other way in which she could have received and absorbed the information:

1. I know tuberculosis makes people lose weight and can kill
2. Dad's kidding me!

The above is a true case although greatly simplified. It needed no peculiar theories to uncover the precise reason for this lady's problem. Only the techniques and understanding of Curative Hypnotherapy were necessary to allow her to recall precisely why and how her computer had **logically** worked to protect her by creating this weight problem.

It did not need much commonsense to correct the sequence of events – but a computer has no commonsense, it has only logic. The patient needed to remember the incident and until then, until the whole incident was recalled, she was unable to correct her reaction.

Although this may appear a simple case, it is no more simple than a case of persistent headaches or anxiety or depression. All of these are logical reactions based on wrong information.

So how does it help to classify a patient? Was the above lady oral, anal, genital, comical, Neanderthal or digital? How would a therapist's (NOT the patient's) classification of her character alter their approach in treatment – surely this could only be to the sufferer's detriment. The lady had made a **unique** mistake in the sequence of events. Unless this was uncovered she could not be cured.

What would be the next step for a therapist after putting this lady into one of these theoretical pigeon holes? There can only be two ways to treat a patient's problem. A therapist has to either find the cause or treat the symptom (whether suppression by direct suggestion or persuading the patient to accept a substitute symptom).

In the above case the therapist could induce hypnosis and, by-passing the conscious mind, attempt to suppress the overeating. While this is going on the computer is working at lightning speed to see if there is an alternative way of avoiding tuberculosis. It will run through the memory banks to see if there is any other way of by-passing the threatened death by TB. It is programmed to do everything possible to protect that person and it will either find another way to protect her or will reject the suggestions of symptom suppression.

This lady became overweight to avoid a fatal disease so consider the following on the assumption that her appetite is suppressed:

"Fresh air and exercise" says her sub-conscious "– that's it! I'll take up jogging. I'll join a gymnasium and do weight-lifting and aerobics." Then with the strain of exerting herself while carrying around 50 excess pounds of fat she develops a heart problem because her sub-conscious turns her into a keep-fit-aholic in its efforts to make her avoid TB.

If she believes in fresh air, does she develop claustrophobia to keep her out in the open?

Or maybe she heard somewhere that drinking sherry was good for the lungs and steadily starts to drink more and more. Our lady could thus easily become an alcoholic.

Or, if a really good job of symptom suppression is done by the therapist and there is no other information available to her about avoiding the problem (bearing in mind that she has no idea that the comments by her father referring to TB were ever made, because the therapist does not have the ability to help her recall this incident), does she develop anxiety expecting some disease or other to strike at any moment now that she is losing weight? Does she become a hypochrondiac? Does she develop a fear of death which could be with her every waking minute?

In looking at the above alternatives you have to bear in mind that the lady went for treatment with a weight problem and that neither the therapist nor the patient has any idea WHY she has the problem.

You also have to remember that she may have a dozen other bits of information that she can use, either individually or in conjunction with others, to create problems that would appear preposterous to the common-sense mind.

All of the alternative problems I have suggested above are worse than being overweight because our living computer is there for our protection. Its sole purpose is to keep us as happy, healthy and safe as it can and will always choose the least distressing way out of any problem.

Hence, when symptoms are suppressed the alternatives developed are very often much worse although, being subconscious reactions, neither the therapist nor the patient realises that the new problem is a substitution and the therapy continues indefinitely: ". . . a marvellous Hypnotherapist. He got rid of my weight problem and then when I got claustrophobia he cleared that up for me. So I'm now going to get rid of my drinking problem. HE ALWAYS CURES ME"!!

Complicated theories are continually expounded without any rhyme or reason and certainly without either logic, common-sense or any attempt to justify the peculiar assumptions.

My practice has, at the same address, the headquarters of the Association of Qualified Curative Hypnotherapists which is the Registered Charity devoted to improving the standards of Hypnotherapy and educating the public to its benefits. We therefore get a lot of phone calls from all parts of the country and, while most of them want us to recommend a Curative Hypnotherapist (we post them a complete register without charge) there is also a steady number of complaints about other people who use Hypnosis and in some cases cause their patients great distress.

"He shouts at me, accusing me of having a guilty secret."
"All she ever does is make me talk about my sexual desires, needs and experiences. She believes that all problems have their root in a sexual incident". "He keeps trying to make me re-experience – actually re-live – the worst thing that ever happened to me and I get really scared. I feel physically sick at the thought of going for treatment".

Without any doubt these therapists are attempting to make their patients fit some theory, and they are going to do their best to MAKE the sufferer fit a nice, neat pigeon-hole no matter what else happens. They are doing exactly what they have been taught to do and do not have the mental ability to think further than what has been pumped into them quite irrespective of the fact that these theories have no foundation whatsoever, and in many cases are cruel in the extreme to the poor people who go to them for help.

However, Hypnotherapy is steadily becoming more accepted and, what is more important, Curative Hypnotherapy is right in the forefront of this progress. This means that more people are becoming **Curative** Hypnotherapists bringing into the profession more people who have their patients' interests at heart and are not prepared to accept teaching without using their own analytical abilities.

This is evidenced by the numbers of people who have been through training courses in the use of Hypnosis and, having realised that their patients are not achieving the results anticipated, are coming on my course to learn how to FIND THE CAUSE TO CURE. Over the last few years a good percentage of those I have trained are people who have undertaken previous courses, of one sort or another, in Hypnosis.

Some of these courses encourage their trainees to use their 'clairvoyant' abilities in treatment. Whether or not this is just a guessing game, it is certainly the therapists' ideas that will prevail. Others use 'free association' on the assumption that if someone talks long enough they will eventually come up with the incident that is the cause of their problem. No wonder this is called the 'thousand hour therapy' and may take from 10 to 20 years!

Apart from changes in the attitude of the therapist during this lengthy period due to his increasing age, the patient himself also matures and his environment must also alter. People he knows die, others come into his life. His social life changes, his working conditions alter and his problem will change as well.

Some therapists use psycho-analysis combined with hypnosis, but psycho-analysis is not really analysis – it involves persuading a patient to fit the therapist's pre-conceived ideas – which are very often based on a sexual theory and it is sickening to have new patients who have been through treatment similar to this who, having been persuaded that they indulged in some sexual perversion, say "what sort of a person can I be if this really happened?"

The volunteers for whom I advertise prove in front of the members of training courses that each individual interprets things in their own way. Everything is interpreted in the light of that person's previous experience and **no two people can possibly have experienced identical events throughout their lives.**

This is proven in public BY THE PATIENTS THEMSELVES.

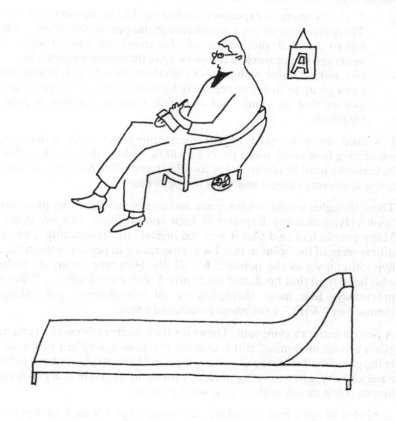

"And how do you respond to these voices in your head?"

Symptom or Cause?

While leaning on the sea-wall of a small holiday resort watching the sail-boards skimming over the bay, the words of a nearby lady made me direct my attention to her conversation with her friend:

".... treatment is expensive, of course, but he doesn't regret it. There is no-one doing acupuncture in this part of the country. He has to travel 80 miles each way for treatment and a couple of years ago he got stuck in the snow up in the mountains for a whole day and got home with greater pain than when he left, but he has been going to this man regularly for more than eleven years and swears that he could not continue working without regular treatment."

I walked away to save myself interrupting her with a lecture, wondering how many more years he will be making this journey. Will he continue until he is too old, or too ill to travel. Will he continue until the acupuncturist dies – and what happens then?

These thoughts would not leave me and comments about my previous book (Hypnotherapy Explained) kept coming back into my mind. Many people had said that it was "so logical" or "fascinating", while others were of the opinion that I was attempting to persuade them that hypnotherapy was the panacea for all ills. However, many of those who have read that book and said "now I understand why . . ." were previously, like most therapists of all persuasions, not asking themselves "WHY" a sufficient number of times.

A person suffers a symptom. They visit their doctor who says a certain gland is malfunctioning. But is that the real reason for their problem? Is the gland malfunction not just a symptom? Does there not have to be a reason why, after working perfectly for many years, that organ is no longer doing its job in the way it was intended?

A patient of mine had visited an acupuncturist and been told that her energy flows were out of balance and could be corrected by that therapist but, as she said, "I want to know why they became unbalanced. Unless this is corrected the problem could keep recurring".

We all accept that the body will do its best to heal itself. If we cut ourselves, we will heal unless the wound is too great. Broken bones will re-knit and if our body is invaded by a virus we will produce anti-bodies to fight off the infection.

But the healing process does not always work, and we should ask "WHY"

The husband of the lady on whom I had been eavesdropping had probably attended his local medical practitioner before starting his travels over the mountains to his 'alternative' therapist. Obviously this acupuncturist was achieving more than his doctor, but it was still only alleviation of his symptoms for a time - it obviously did not cure - the healing process was not taking place and we are compelled to ask "WHY".

Why do so many practitioners of 'alternative' or 'complementary' therapies have long waiting lists for treatment due to 'regular patients'? Why are so many doctor's reception areas occupied by the same people year after year? Why does alleviation of a troublesome symptom not last? Why is it that so many patients have a symptom suppressed only to present themselves for treatment with another complaint?

The answer appears to be simple: the patient has a NEED for their problem and if it is suppressed it will either re-appear or, if a really good job of suppression is done, they will develop a substitute symptom to fulfill this **sub-conscious need.**

I said this was a simple answer but it is this very simplicity which makes the idea hard to accept.

A person presents themselves for treatment and describes to the practitioner (whether acupuncturist, medical doctor, hypnotherapist, homoeopath or other therapist) the symptom for which they wish to have treatment. The practitioner undertakes whatever examination his particular discipline requires and either treats the symptoms directly or discovers that a particular part of the body is malfunctioning or is in imbalance and then proceeds to treat that malfunction regarding it as the cause of the problem. Yet there has to be a reason for that part of the body not working properly.

After all, the patient is putting into his body the same substances that he always has (the same food, drink and air) and is doing the same activities as he has done for years. He has suffered no physical injuries and his body should, therefore, be functioning in exactly the same way as it has in the past after allowing for the wear and tear of the natural ageing process. So what has changed to create their discomfort? Why does the patient suddenly create a 'malfunction' when the same materials are being consumed in exactly the same way and nothing else appears to have altered? And why does one person develop a problem when a similar person, consuming the same fuel and with an almost identical life-style, experience no symptoms?

Does not the cause of the problem have to lie in the patients 'control centre'?

When my patients tell me that they are in a 'very stressful occupation' I ask them whether others that they work with, and are doing identical jobs, experience the same trouble that has brought them to me for treatment. The reply is always that they do not appear to have the same problems and, in saying this, my patient is actually saying that he or she realises the cause of their problem lies **in themselves** not in their job.

The cause of their problem lies not in the 'stressful job' but in their reaction to it. There has to be something that is making them react to this occupation by developing their symptom. It is my task to enable the patient to find out why they have this abnormal reaction.

The man who says that after a couple of drinks he is unable to stop, is always asked by me whether his drinking friends have a similar problem. If not, the reason does not lie in the addictive quality of alcohol but in my patient. To simply suppress the desire for drink or to create an aversion to alcohol is to leave the cause of his problem untouched to create further problems in the future.

The woman who experiences difficulty when attempting sexual intercourse is highly unlikely to have anything physically wrong with her. Her body will almost certainly be found to be normally formed and the nerves intact. The problem lies in the way that the messages carried to her brain are interpreted or in the messages sent back in response through her nerves from her control centre to the parts of her body that have the apparent wrong reaction.

To treat such a person with standard sex therapy (such as sensate focusing) is to treat her symptom – to almost attempt to force her to enjoy intercourse – and does nothing about why she has developed her problem. If sometime in the past she has absorbed information that sex is better avoided (whether for moral, physical or emotional reasons) but is put in the position of being 'forced' to enjoy it she could easily create anything from recurring genital rashes to obesity in order to make herself unattractive to the opposite sex.

A cream from her doctor may help the rash. Starvation diets may reduce her weight but there are plenty of other ways that her subconscious can find to prevent her doing what it 'believes' is wrong, dirty, painful or sinful. The only way to overcome the problem completely and permanently is to find out what has caused this belief, and thus the wrong reaction, in the first place.

We know that pain is felt in the mind. If you accidentally touch something extremely hot, messages are flashed to your brain. Messages that not only make you feel the pain but also make you take action to remove your hand from danger. You jerk your hand away without conscious thought and, if the hot article is being held, you will unclasp your hand to let it go. If, however, the hot thing is touched with the fingertips of your outstretched hand then you may do the opposite – clench your hand as you pull it away. Without any conscious thought whatsoever you will take whatever action appears most likely to minimise pain and injury.

Reflex actions. Actions without conscious thought. Sub-conscious actions. Computer reactions because speed is necessary to prevent damage so far as is possible. There is no time to analyse what is creating the pain because damage may result from the delay.

But cut the nerves that carry the message of that heat from finger tips to brain and none of these things occur. There will be no feeling of pain therefore the brain does not recognise danger and takes no avoiding action.

All pain is experienced by the mind, yet often people present themselves for treatment of pain for which the medical profession can find no physical cause. The most usual procedure is for them to be prescribed 'painkillers' to mask the discomfort. Their physician has satisfied himself that there is no physical cause and is well aware that pain is experienced in the mind yet only a few enlightened doctors will suggest that the reason for the pain be investigated in the place where it originates. The majority satisfy themselves with drugging the symptom. (There are apparently 6322 million pain-killers taken in the U.K. every year – compare that to our population of around 60 million and bear in mind that many people never take any!)

Some of my ex-patients recognised themselves from the descriptions of their cases in my previous book (no-one else could have identified them as all details were deliberately altered to preserve anonymity). The fact that some of them were able to identify themselves shows the unique way each person creates their problem, and an example of this turned up on a training course a couple of years ago.

A lady with hay fever had just left the premises after her third treatment and, as we had a few minutes before the next patient was due to arrive, I was telling the course members about a man who had created hay fever to keep him out of his garden because, as a young child, he had damaged his eye with a glass splinter in the shed at the bottom of his garden. I will not bother to give the full case here because the point of this story is that, in the middle of my explanation as to how and why hay fever had been created, one of the members of the course said he knew about whom I was talking. Apparently, the full story had been recounted to him by my patient and it was because of his cure that my interrupter had been recommended to come on the training course. He added that the day before he had seen my ex-patient cutting his grass without any vestige of hay fever.

His reason for hay-fever was unique to him, which made him identifiable by his friend to whom he had explained his treatment.

"But hay fever is an allergic reaction not a mental one" is a common remark.

So why do some people develop streaming eyes and runny nose when in a room with a vase of flowers – until they are told, and are able to satisfy themselves, that the flowers are artificial; when their symptoms will disappear?

Is this the same type of reaction as a person whose mouth waters at some of the beautifully produced pictures of tempting food in the more up-market womens' magazines.

These people do not need the saliva they produce. They do not intend to tear out the page and eat it, but a message reaches the brain that says 'food' or, in the case of hay-fever, it says 'pollen' or some such message. Whether the message reaches the brain through the sense of sight or the sense of smell is not important. The brain recognises the stimulus and produces whatever it is programmed to produce whether sneezing or saliva.

Let us think about allergies for a few moments. Someone who changes neither their life-style, the way they use their body nor the food that they eat may, without any previous sign, develop an allergy. What has happened to cause this reaction? What is the best way to tackle it? I repeat – nothing has changed. The food is the same, the processes of digestion and absorbtion are just as they have been for the past 27 years otherwise there would be a change in the reaction to all foods.

Their job has not altered and the relationships between colleagues at work and in the home and social environment remain as before. The air being breathed is the same, not only to what our sufferer has breathed in the past but also the same as everyone else is inhaling – and everyone else has not developed an allergy. Nothing, in fact, has altered – except the reaction. This reaction cannot, therefore, be a physical one, and consequently must be mental. A mental reaction which is causing a physical symptom.

On the assumption that we are now dealing with a food allergy we can now find out to what they are allergic. They can then avoid this food in the future.

Is that a cure? Is that not more like taking the ladder away from a person with a fear of heights? They will not experience the fear caused by being up high – but the fear is still there. If you don't believe that – then give them back the ladder and tell them to climb!

One of the trainees on my course in 1988 was telling us about his daughter who had developed allopecia at about 9 years old. All the hair had fallen out of the childs head. An allergy to a particular type of food was diagnosed, this was removed from the childs diet and gradually her hair renewed itself. Months later it all fell out again so – back to the allergy clinic – where it was discovered that not only was she now allergic to a different kind of food but she no longer had an adverse reaction to the food that had been denied her.

This girl obviously had a 'need' for her symptom and preventing her reacting in the way that her sub-conscious had worked out was most certainly not a cure. Sympton substitution will occur in cases of avoidance like this just as often as it will if a really good job of symptom suppression is done.

A person with hay fever who takes anti-histamine or other 'remedy' or lives in a controlled atmosphere may not suffer their symptoms but the problem remains and if they give up their medication or leave their sterile environment they will re-experience them once again.

In fact, measures like these do nothing to actually solve the problem because, in a large number of cases, when an allergic reaction is denied to somebody by avoidance they will develop an allergy to another substance.

Does it not make more sense to find the cause of the allergy? The cause that lies in the mind – the sub-conscious; which can only be investigated through the use of hypnosis.

It is natural to feel anxiety in certain situations, natural to feel depressed if you lose your job or a loved one, and if you did not have natural tension you would never achieve anything in your life. These are normal mental reactions and when they become exaggerated and grow into a problem is it not more sensible to look for the mental cause rather than to try physical treatments like changes of diet or pills, neither of which can cure?

Everyone accepts that the mind controls many physical processes. The mental emotion of embarrassment causes the physical reaction of blushing and often sweating as well. We know that mental stress can cause ulcers, that fear alters our breathing rate, sorrow causes our eyes to water (tears), fright changes the heart beat, visual stimuli cause physical sexual reactions, stress can cause high blood pressure. seeing someone vomit can cause the feeling that you want to be sick, terror can create diarrhoea and the sight of blood makes some people go 'weak at the knees' just as the sight of food will make their mouth water.

Every part of your body is controlled by your mind — every muscle, every nerve, every gland responds to what goes on in your computer.

Eczema, asthma and psoriasis are called 'nervous complaints' but does that mean there is something wrong with your nerves or that you are a timid (nervous) person? Of course that catch-all expression does not mean anything of the sort. After all, what are your nerves? They are only carriers of messages just as are the wires that carry electricity around your house. These message carriers will do nothing except carry messages. Therefore the cause of any trouble has to lie at either the transmitting or the receiving end. What this term 'nervous complaint' really means is that the nerves are carrying a wrong message so should we not look at the point of origin of the message to find the fault?

On page 29 of the book "Nymphomania" by Albert Ellis and Edward Sagarin (Ortolan Press) the authors describe nymphomania as "caused by unusual condition of neuro-muscular disease." They state that it is "more a physiological than a psychological disease." They are putting the blame on muscles. They know that muscles are controlled by nerves but they cannot take the obvious next step of asking why the nerves are carrying wrong messages.

Most practitioners of all therapies are unable to take that additional step of asking 'why'. If they did so they would realise that all physical processes have to be controlled and that control lies in the automatic part of the mind — the part that we cannot consciously control ourselves, the part that is only available for examination through the use of hypnosis.

Unfortunately, I have to lump the majority of hypnotherapists with the practitioners of other therapies mentioned in the last paragraph as they also appear to have difficulty in understanding that trying to blast symptoms out of existence with 'direct suggestion' is no better than symptom alleviation by any other means, and that to try to make a patient fit the therapist's particular theory will often create more problems than they temporarily alleviate.

Continuously we should be asking WHY? The cure for an allergy cannot be avoidance – there is a reason WHY. Masking depression by drugging a patient cannot be the real answer, which is to find out WHY. We need to think about the true reason for problems and not mix symptoms with causes. The cause of a problem cannot be glandular misfunction – that is only a symptom. We need to find out WHY that gland is not doing its proper job. You have to FIND THE **TRUE** CAUSE TO CURE.

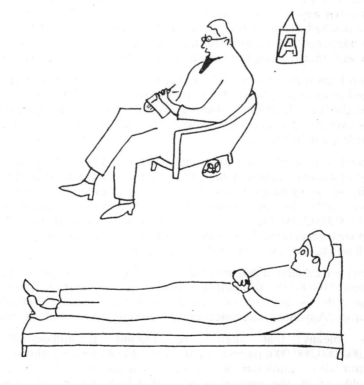

"I have an unnatural desire to feature in a cartoon"

The Memory Game

"Far to the north, in the land called Svithjod, lies a black rock, one hundred miles high and one hundred miles wide. Once every ten thousand years, a little bird flies to the rock and sharpens it beak. When all the rock has been worn away, one second of one day of eternity will have gone by."

I do not know the origin of the above quotation and you may be wondering about its' relevance to Curative Hypnotherapy.

There is no relevance between the precise meaning of those words and my job, but if you substitute our understanding of the brain for 'eternity' it neatly sums up how far I believe we have gone in our investigation of the human mind.

Patients will often confess to having a poor memory: "But I can't remember anything at all before I was eight" they may say when we have reached a stage in therapy where they have recalled an incident that happened when they were that age and we have established that they were then reacting to an incident that had previously taken place.

When I tell them that everything that they have ever experienced is stored away in their head, they express disbelief. Yet I have only told them the truth. Everything that they have ever seen, everything they have ever heard, every smell, taste and tactile sensation is stored and therefore can be recalled.

According to a television programme (20.Sept.1988 BBC2), at one stage of its development, a human foetus creates a quarter of a million brain cells **every minute.** The same programme quoted the number of these cells in an adult as one-hundred-thousand-million (100,000,000,000). Figures I have come across in my reading vary this number from several times as many down to half this quantity. Let us work on the smallest number that I have found quoted:

It has been calculated that our brain has approximately fifty-thousand-million (50,000,000,000) neurons (brain cells) and that each one of those cells has upwards of a thousand (some as many as 60,000) synapses. A synapse is a connection between one neuron and another.

This means that there are around ten-million-million (10,000,000,000,000) pathways and, as at the end of each pathway is a neuron with a minimum of at least a thousand further paths as a possible route, the number of ways that information can be put together completely defeats someone with my mathematical abilities.

In "Robot and Meaning" by Kai Falkman (Bachman & Turner), the author quotes a far higher number of circuits in the human brain – 125 million billion and adds "researchers in microtechnology expect to be able soon to create millions, and later billions of circuits in microcomputers".

Our technical experts are a long way from creating anything as powerful as the millions of billions of circuits said to be in the human brain which, it has been calculated (by some means that I cannot understand), can store up to 800 memories a second. It would, so I have read, need a computer the height of a two storey building covering an area of 67 square kilometres which would consume two-thousand-million watts of electricity – the equivalent of every house in Britain having well over a hundred one-bar fires burning all at the same time.

The Sunday Telegraph Magazine on 12th. June 1988 quoted post-mortem records as showing that the average weight of the male brain was 3lb 0.4oz in 1860 and has increased to 3lb 2.2oz in 1987 and that the female brain has increased from 2lb 11.8oz to 2lb 12.6 oz. If we assume the same rate of growth then, in the 7 years since "Robot and Meaning" was published, we should have developed many millions of new pathways over the amount quoted by Kai Falkman.

However, all these figures are meaningless so I thought that I would try to bring those mind-boggling numbers down to the sort of scale that I could understand and I thought of the life-span of Homo Sapiens.

I started with the biblical life-span of 'three score years and ten' simply because I do not know the average life expectancy in our modern world and it seemed a nice round number.

A person who lives 70 years will experience 2,207,520,000 seconds of time during this period.

Now let us get rid of all the unneccessary zeros and superfluous numbers, and say that a person lives for 2-thousand-million seconds and has in their brain 5O-thousand-million neurons which is the lowest number I have found recorded. This means that each and every one of us has twenty-five times as many brain cells as there are seconds in our life.

Or, to put it another way, on the assumption that each neuron stores and reacts to only one bit of information, we could experience, absorb AND REMEMBER **25 different things every second of our lives** – even when we are asleep or under anaesthetic.

As we are talking of differing interpretations we could look at it in this way: If we experienced two sensations with each of our five senses (taste, touch, smell, sight, hearing) every second of our life, (even when asleep), we would have to live to the ripe old age of 175 years to use all our neurons if each neuron stored and reacted to only one bit of information.

And each one of those bits of information is linked to at least a thousand more.

I have deliberately taken the lowest number of neurons that I have found quoted. Some researchers put the number several times as high, and as each neuron has between a thousand and sixty-thousand synapses, any increase in the number of neurons causes a multiplication of the information that we can remember and of the amount of ways that we may interpret the information that we absorb. This would mean a multiplication of our possible reactions – not just an addition.

I feel like apologising for bringing numbers into this book, particularly when we are not interested in the mechanics of the brain but in its effect. However, I hope that you may now be able to accept that everything that happens to us or around us, everything that we experience through all of our five senses is stored in the memory banks of our personal computers and can be recalled – all it needs is the right techniques.

In "The Shape of Minds to Come", (Weybright & Talley), John G.Taylor quotes the words of Sir Charles Sherrington who describes the capacity of our brain in more poetic language than I can:

> ". . . an enchanted loom where millions of flashing shuttles weave
> a dissolving pattern, always meaningful though
> never an abiding one."

These words were written by a physiologist, a person who is more interested in physical aspects than mental ones but he expresses it beautifully and the reason why the pattern is never 'an abiding one' is because we are continuously adding new experiences, altering our interpretations, and changing our reactions.

When one thinks of the amount of information that a person has stored, is it any wonder that some of it is wrong? Would it not be amazing if, with all the information stored being interconnected with every other bit of information, all the interpretations we make were correct? Some of the information we receive has to be interpreted incorrectly because, all the time, our computers are trying to fit it in with previous information, previous experiences; and no two people have ever had exactly the same experiences. Hence, every person has a slightly different interpretation of everything.

Add to the above the fact that we all start off with slightly different genetic make-up. John Brierley in his book "The Thinking Machine" (Heineman) says "each sperm and egg contains unique combinations of genetic information on the chromosones. In fact the probability of one sperm or egg having the same assortment of parental chromosones is one in 8,388,608".

So we start off slightly different and from the moment of birth our experiences are different thus our interpretations of everything must be slightly different. In other words every person is **UNIQUE,** and makes unique interpretations and if everyone makes slightly different interpretations of the same happening then it follows that some of them must be wrong and it is this unique interpretation that can create a problem.

Some of these problems are mental, some emotional and some are physical.

Is that really true?

If a person suffers anxiety – that is a mental problem, isn't it? But if when they have an anxiety attack they experience stomach cramps, or palpitations or breathlessness – are not those physical problems?

If they have a lack of confidence – that is mental. But if they develop heavy sweating when they meet situations where confidence is needed – isn't that physical?

I do not intend to labour this point.
Everything that goes on in your body is controlled by your mind
and
Everything without an external cause must have an internal one.

The list of physical effects that are created by the mind is endless. The inter-reaction between mind and body is unbelievably close.

The use of Hypnosis is, therefore, too complex to be regarded as magic yet there are Hypnotherapists who advertise that they will cure nail-biting or examination nerves with just one treatment.

It is quite possible to suppress a symptom in one session, depending on how receptive the patient may be. But I well remember a lady who came to me with eczema on the back of her hands and on her face. As we investigated it turned out that this was only a substitute for nail biting that had been 'cured' in two sessions of simple hypnotic 'direct suggestion' by a doctor who uses hypnosis.

But she had been 'cured' of nail-biting. Unless, of course, she has similar symptom suppression for eczema and substitutes a blushing/ sweating problem and then, when that is suppressed develops, guess what? – Nail-biting. The variations of this type of scenario are endless.

Many therapists will use hypnosis to instruct a patient's computer to get rid of a symptom and, depending on how strong the 'need' for the symptom may be or the alternative symptoms that may be available in the memory banks, it may be effectively suppressed.

The therapist tells the patient that they are 'cured' and feels that their fee has been well earned. The patient, believing that the therapist is an expert, accepts their word and leaves with diminished, or even completely without, symptoms. At least they leave with the belief that, even though it may take some time for their problem to disappear completely, it will go.

Three possibilities are now obvious:

(1)　The problem goes, does not return in the future, and no substitute symptom appears to develop.

(2)　The symptoms recur some time in the future

(3)　the symptoms disappear but another problem is substituted

Let us look at those alternatives in a little more detail: Whether a patient consciously realises it or not, their problem is almost certainly a reaction to something external. It is possible that this reason for their reaction has ceased to exist and the symptom is, therefore, no longer necessary. They have simply been holding onto a habit.

A habit without any purpose can easily be stopped by hypnosis if the patient wishes to lose it. But how can a therapist be certain that it has no purpose unless a proper job of investigation is done? The nail-biter I have mentioned could have developed this habit when a child as a reaction to some particular piece of authoritarian discipline by an adult.

But she is now an adult herself. She is no longer subject to the authority of her 'elders and betters' as she used to be. The adult in question may even have been dead for years.

Almost certainly, simple habit breaking would suffice in this case. But how does the therapist know what is creating her problem without finding out from the part of her mind which has the information? – Her sub-conscious. There is no good listening to what she brings up from her conscious mind – if the reason for her problem was there then it would be useless using hypnosis in treatment. After all, hypnosis is relaxing the conscious mind to allow direct access to the subconscious. To go back to our analogy: If the computer-operator is mis-reading the information that comes from the computer there is no use seeking an error in the data in the computer itself.

Conversely, if the computer has wrong information then it is useless to try to find out what this is from the operator. If the operator knew all the information in the computer and how it put all these bits of data together, then he would not need the computer. And, of course, our human operator believes what is in his personal memory banks.

So a habit could be broken completely and permanently with 'direct suggestion' but the therapist cannot know without a proper investigation of the sub-conscious whether it is complete and whether it is permanent.

The problem goes. Our nail-biter changes her job. Her new boss is a very authoritarian figure and treats her in a similar way to the manner in which she was treated as a child. She is back to her nail biting because nothing was done about the CAUSE.

Or a really good job of suppression was done and instead of nail biting she develops hair-pulling, chewing the inside of her cheeks – or eczema, or tension pains in her neck and shoulders or . . .?

Many patients treated by Curative Hypnotherapy will completely lose their problems WITHOUT ANY SYMPTOM TREATMENT whatsoever. Once the CAUSE has been corrected, once the need for the symptom has gone, the problem will automatically disappear, although it is sometimes a big help to give it a good push in the right direction at the end of the treatment.

Hypnosis is not magic. There is no substitute for logical, methodical working through the treatment to ensure that any and every cause of the problem has been disposed of. For instance in the case of migraine, once the cause of the problem has been uncovered by the patient, and then corrected, a good Curative Hypnotherapist will always ensure:

> that the incident cannot cause migraine in the future
> that there is no incident which will prevent the patient losing migraine
> that there is no other incident that could cause migraine in the future
> that the patient can lose their migraine completely
> that the patient can lose their migraine permanently

that the patient will lose it completely and permanently
that there is nothing to prevent this taking place
and so on. Checking, double-checking, cross-checking again and again
because one never knows how a person is interpreting the questions.
Asking in as many different ways as possible because there are times
when, just as you are ready to finish the very last treatment, you will
get an answer that completely deflates you. The patient's
understanding of your question has been different to the meaning you
put on it.

But before getting to this stage one has to enable the patient to recall
the precise incident – not what they think may be creating their
problem (if they knew the cause they would have corrected the trouble
for themselves), not what the therapist believes may be creating the
symptoms (how can he or she possibly know?). The only way to cure
anything is to first find out the cause. Whether it is a car that won't
start, a television that will not produce a picture or a person with a
wrong reaction. To cure you have to find the cause.

And, of course, it is necessary to ensure that this information comes
from the subconscious.

A Curative Hypnotherapist should have the ability to enable the
patient to uncover the cause of a problem so that it can be corrected.
They will not treat the symptoms of anxiety, depression, asthma or
pre-menstrual tension (if this were natural then every woman would
suffer). They will use their skill to find out 'why' so that **the cause can be
put right.**

The Importance of 'Why?'

Many people using hypnosis as a therapy believe that it is necessary for a person having treatment to experience 'emotion while in the chair', yet emotion gets in the way of treatment, slows down progress and, most damaging of all, can be so strong that the patient believes that this incident has to be the cause of the problem and, as the therapist has this belief before even starting treatment, they both go swiftly along a false trail. The therapist will believe he is doing a good job and the patient is content because the treatment is emotionally painful and, therefore must be doing him good!

Sometimes a new patient at the first consultation will say they have come for Hypnotherapy because they had the same problem in the past and were 'cured' by Hypnotherapy. One is tempted to ask: "If you have been cured – what are you doing here with the same problem?"

Others will come with a problem which is a direct result of a previous Hypnotherapist persuading the patient to relive horrific events so that, in desperation, they have got rid of their original symptom to give themselves the excuse to cease treatment – and then developed a different symptom as a replacement.

Yet again, some will say "I cannot believe the things that I re-lived really happened. Yet they must be true or I could not have remembered them, could I?"

Some patients, of course, have been completely confused – "the therapist kept accusing me of having a guilty secret until I told him of an incident that I'm not sure really happened. But the fact that I could think up something so terrible makes me wonder what sort of person I really am."

Time after time one hears hypnotherapists talking about "releasing repressions" and getting people to relive traumatic events. "Experience again the most terrible event of your whole life. Feel again the same feeling that you had at that time". This is probably the most horrible thing that one can do with hypnosis – my word for it is cruel. It is doubly cruel when you consider that the therapist does this without first establishing whether this event, even if a real happening, is the cause of the problem.

Quite often, of course, a traumatic event may be the 'trigger' or, at least have something to do with the creation of a problem. But this cannot be assumed to be the case as, just as often, there is no really traumatic event at all. In any case is it not likely that, because a person has a problem, they will react to future incidents with ever increasing emotions. (A bad experience in a certain situation leads to an expectation of a further bad reaction in similar circumstances, and the problem escalates.) Hence there is a good chance that the "most terrifying happening in their life" took place AFTER the incident that really lies at the root of their problem. So even if this incident does have a bearing on the creation of their trouble, the therapist is well off target from the word 'go'.

To accuse a person of having a "guilty secret" when there is no evidence that guilt lies at the root of the problem and it may just as easily be jealousy, embarrassment, shame, insecurity or any other emotion, is making the patient follow a false trail which cannot cure him.

Not only is there a danger that the therapist will lead the patient astray but also the fact that if a patient is 'pushed' he may start to give the therapist the information that he believes the therapist wants. Before treatment has progressed very far, imagination is building fantasy upon fantasy. The patient gives the therapist the information that he believes the therapist wants. The therapist believes the patient and his line of questioning or suggestions makes this obvious to the sufferer who then starts to believe that his fantasy is actually fact. A completely muddled patient eventually emerges from therapy, believing that a cure has been effected because the 'expert' has said so, yet still suffering from a problem that has probably altered in nature but is still a problem.

A good hypnotherapist will be very careful not to lead their patient. **ONLY the patient knows how they have created their problem** and it is the therapist's job to help them recall that precise event. The only person who can possibly have this information is the person with the problem, so almost any suggestion by the therapist must be leading on a false trail, and many times on training courses I have said – and the patients have demonstrated – that **it is rarely a traumatic event that actually creates a problem.**

From time to time those who have been on my training course have telephoned me to say they have a problem with a patient. This, I am pleased to say, is an unusual occurence and normally my advice consists of just three words.

These queries are usually something on the lines of:

> "I have a patient with a fear of heights, who took me back to when he was trapped in a lift on the fifteenth floor of a block of

flats when he was a kid. Although he has told me about this, and
we have worked on it, I cannot enable him to get rid of his fear.
What should I do ?"

or

"Someone has a fear of flying and keeps referring to a very
bumpy and frightening experience in an airplane. We keep going
back to this experience but seem to be getting nowhere."

They ask me what they should do and my answer is normally just three
words – **"find out why"**.

A plane with a hundred and thirty three people on board has a very
bumpy trip, and one of the passengers develops a fear of flying
afterwards. The other 132 do not, so there has to be a reason why that
one is reacting in the way they are. There is something else in their
mind to which they are reacting. The trip itself is only the trigger. It is
the job of the therapist to enable their patient to pin-point the first step
on the path to developing their problem. Not what triggers their
symptoms but what loads their gun for them in the first place.

On the subject of fear of flying I would like to bring in here a case
mentioned in 'Hypnotherapy' by Dave Elman (Westwood Publishing,
Glendale, Calif). On page 182 he states that he believes that his own
fear of flying is caused by an occasion when he and his wife went to the
airport with their son who was joining a couple of plane-loads of other
students.

After the planes had taken off, but before he and his wife had left the
airport, it was announced that one of the planes had crashed. He later
found out that his son was safe and sound in the other plane – but he
believes that this is the cause of his flying phobia!

He does not ask himself whether all parents with student offspring on
the same plane now have the same fear. There is even no mention of
his wife developing the same phobia yet she went through the identical
incident, hearing the same announcement and sharing the rest of the
experience as must have other parents of students on both the doomed
plane and the one carrying his son.

If all these people do not have the same phobia as the author then does
there not have to be something else in his mind to which he is reacting?

Case after case in this book appears to demonstrate that much closer
consideration would be necessary before drawing the conclusions
arrived at by Mr. Elman.

He talks about a woman (page 76) who did not secrete sufficient saliva to wear dentures, yet produced enough to swallow and digest food. Under what he calls 'hypnoanalysis' she revealed that 25 years previously she'd had her tonsils out and believed that the surgeon's hands were dirty. Under local anaesthetic, she insisted he wash his hands and then re-sterilize his equipment – "Have you ever noticed that when you are afraid your mouth gets dry?" he asks, "I am of the opinion that she is abreacting to the tonsillectomy . . . an almost constant panic when anything comes near her mouth".

Notice that this is HIS OPINION – he does not find out from the patient. Note also his further comment that this hallucination of uncleanliness was "triggered by fear of the operation". No thought of trying to find out what caused such an unnatural fear that a quarter of century later it is still causing her a problem.

What sort of reaction is this person going to have if major surgery is ever needed. He does not enable her to cure her fear, merely suppresses the saliva problem.

Continually, in this book, the author gives cases of tinkering with symptoms: A girl of 14 got scarlet fever, worried about after effects and therefore became overweight (page 169). Does this not mean that anyone who catches scarlet fever should put on weight?

On page 199 he talks about a woman whose aunt died. According to Elman it was the Aunts liking for roses that caused his patient's rose fever! I'll make no further comment – just think about it.

However, Mr. Elman goes even further in this book and the following transcript is enlightening. Having said to a patient "I don't want to put words into your mouth", he then proceeds to do exactly that:

ELMAN: "In other words, what I'm getting at – this dermatitis condition – say it very bluntly – what does it represent? A sort of punishment for what happened".
PATIENT: "I hadn't thought of it that way".
ELMAN: "Well, is that the way you've been thinking about it?"
PATIENT: "I thought it was tied up with whatever prevented me from delivering *(her baby)*. I thought it was hormones".

Elman then pushes her hard with a full eleven lines of uninterrupted verbal pressure, ending up with ". . . you felt that you could have been responsible? Wasn't that the feeling? Was that the feeling that you had?"

Then, having managed to get the patient to accept this:

ELMAN: "Would you call it a guilt complex?"

PATIENT: "Yes".

ELMAN: "That's the term I'm hitting at".

In my opinion a straightforward case of bending a patient to fit his pre-conceived ideas. Never mind why or how the patient actually created her dermatitis. Never mind finding the cause. He had decided at the very beginning that her problem was caused by guilt and he was determined from the start that she should agree to "the term I'm hitting at".

It is a distressing thought that several training courses in the use of hypnosis teach this mans methods. A man who bends people in this way or who does not have the ability to think beyond what triggers a problem (he even uses the word 'trigger' in the above case of the lady with the dry mouth).

Surely those who profess to teach should take the time to think about their subject and not pass on second-hand ideas about getting someone to fit the therapists' theories or supressing symptoms by de-activating one particular trigger.

Remember, talking of guns and triggers – if you deal with a trigger, you are still leaving the gun loaded for something else to come along and fire it. If you go back and unload the gun, then no amount of triggers are going to have any effect what-so-ever. It is the therapists job to unload the gun, not simply confining himself to dealing with the trigger.

A case from my own practice was a lady who had pyrophobia (a fear of fire) which a few years previously, had developed into a fear of electrical things. Her psychiatrist had called her problem 'agoraphobia' because of the continual need to go back and check the electric switches in her house after she had left home. Her life was becoming a real misery as she could not go out without worrying about the electrics and, of course, she had the overwhelming fear of fire as well.

During treatment, she recalled when she was in the Anderson shelter during the war, when her brother opened the door of the shelter and, to use her words, "The sky was aflame" and her brother said "it's not much of a raid because there are no big bangs."

She referred to this incident for the whole of two or three sessions. She would not recall any other incident, either before or after, and one can see how an incendiary raid with the sky aflame could have a connection with a fear of fire. But, I've seen the sky aflame, as have millions of other people, and I am well aware that to develop these problems, as a result of this scene is not a normal reaction – so there had to be something else in her mind to which she was reacting and I had to keep investigating. Having brought back this memory, we were still no nearer enabling her to lose her problem and then, after several sessions just recalling this same scene she eventually remembered when she and her brother and other friends of theirs were playing 'mummies and daddies' in the shelter, and she had a fear that her brother was going to tell their parents. A simple connection between the guilt of what she was doing and the Anderson shelter.

There was fire when she was in the air-raid shelter, a fear of her parents finding out what she had been doing in the shelter, and her brother featured in the incendiary raid scene because he was the person who posed the threat. This threat was not of bombing, not of fire but of her parents finding out what she had been up to.

The traumatic event was the bombing and the sky being aflame, but the incident which really caused the problem was the fear of her brother telling her parents about her sexual explorations. Yet the event that lay at the root of this fear was NOT traumatic, **she enjoyed it immensely** and it was only well after this took place that she started to worry about her brother 'letting the cat out of the bag' because she tried to force him to play the same game again and he did not want to. On this occasion there was no trauma either – all she felt was disappointment. It was only afterwards that she started to worry – if he was not interested, would he tell?

A therapist has to be continually asking himself whether other people would react in the same way to whatever incident the patient brings up. Whether the patient gives the information from the conscious or the sub-conscious it is necessary to see the logic of the reactions. If the person is reacting in a different way to the one in which the majority of other people would be expected to react, then this is an abnormal reaction and there has to be a reason for it. There has to be something else that they have put together with the incident they have divulged.

Recently trained practioners who have telephoned for help will know that my three word answer is normally all that is required – FIND OUT WHY. Obviously there will be times when a patient keeps bringing up the same scene over and over again and even a good hypnotherapist who is using Curative methods becomes caught up in the ever-decreasing circle but the fact that a patient may go back on several different sessions to one particular incident, is no guarantee that the incident referred to is the one which is creating the problem or that everything about that incident has been divulged.

In the cases in this book that I have treated personally, and therefore know all relevant details you will find that the most traumatic event was certainly not the incident which was creating the problem. To deal with the trauma would be to leave these people with their gun still loaded awaiting something else to come along and trigger another problem.

For instance – if the pyrophobic's fear of fire was simply suppressed, she could have developed a sexual problem because of her fear of being found out playing her sex games. She may have developed claustrophobia because it took place in the confined space of the shelter. Or a myriad of other possible symptoms could have replaced the pyrophobia that she had.

It is interesting that the pyrophobic's psychiatrist had told her that she suffered from agoraphobia and that her need to continually return to her house to check that all electric appliances and switches were turned off was just a symptom of her fear of the outside world which was making her retreat into the haven of her own four walls. Whereas, in fact, the incident that caused her fear occurred in the confined space of an air-raid shelter and her fear was actually of leaving her home, of something happening indoors. Not quite, but very nearly, the **exact opposite of the psychiatrist's diagnosis.** A very good example of trying to treat the computer-operator when the misinformation lay in the computer and a glaring example to Hypnotherapists not to work on the diagnosis of someone who has been unable to completely solve a patient's problem.

Curative Hypnotherapy – our method of handling people and their problems – is different to that of other therapies because we insist on finding out the reason why – the **TRUE** reason why – not necessarily of a traumatic event, not necessarily a sexual event, not necessarily anything that created a feeling of guilt, but THE incident – however insignificant it may be – that first started the person on the path to developing their problem. These are the techniques we demonstrate on the training course and are, in fact the sole reason for the establishment of the Association of Qualified Curative Hypnotherapists, and the real meaning behind it's motto – 'FIND THE CAUSE TO CURE'.

Talk to any Hypnotherapist and they will say that they cure – question them carefully and you will find out that those who do are very few indeed. They may deal with a traumatic event, irrespective of whether it is the real cause or not. They may get the patient to fit their pre-conceived ideas, to believe that they will lose their problem – or even that they never had one in the first place! They may blast the symptoms out of the way with direct suggestion without bothering about the consequences. They may use methods such as NLP (Neuro Linguistic Programming) to persuade the patient to accept or create a substitute symptom, or a different behavioural pattern. They may get their patient to imagine that they have lost the problem. But few appear to have the ability to find out the real reason WHY, or may be it is the understanding that they lack. But there is a reason, a logical reason, and the misinformation on which this logic is working has to be corrected to effect a cure.

Suppression of a problem will result in a recurrence in the future or its replacement by an alternative complaint. Substitution of symptoms by any means still leaves the cause to fester, and there is, of course, always a good chance that some time in the future, the substitute will be found to be insufficient or ineffective – with obvious results.

The number of those who telephone for help after completing our course is very small but all of us can get 'too close to the wood to see the trees' at times. When this happens a good therapist will stop, will step back, and will then ask WHY. The sub-conscious is a computer. The sub-conscious is logical and therefore it must be working on some incorrect information. This wrong data has to be uncovered to enable the patient to correct the illogicality of their reaction.

It is an interesting thought that, whereas most teaching of hypnotherapy is done by lecture, by reading and play-acting, we teach by working with **strangers** who have genuine problems. We teach by proving (yes, actually **proving**) that Curative methods get the results we claim. Members of our training courses see it work, they know it works and they gain the ability to find the TRUE CAUSE to enable their patients to achieve a CURE.

Hypnosis and Mysticism

This chapter will, I know, make some people very annoyed but the object of this book is not to please anyone but to attempt to shed some light on hypnosis and its uses, and to try to help those people who need Hypnotherapy to find their way through the minefield. To assist them to sort the wheat from the chaff, the sheep from the goats, the Hypnotist from the Hypnotherapist and the Hypnotherapist from the Curative Hypnotherapist.

Hypnosis has always been associated with mysticism, with controlling another person's mind, in subjugating their will and, because it has been used in the main by people who needed to have some show of power they have built a mystery around it. It was this mysticism that gave them their power. If everyone knew how to induce hypnosis in others they felt that they would lose their status.

Amongst the many people who apply to come on my training courses are a number who have a belief in 'past lives' and various aspects of the occult.

If I can be sure that they are not going to bring their beliefs into treatment, then I might accept them on the course – but most of them I turn down because they will not be using hypnosis to help others but to bolster their own convictions. Their basic confidence is insufficient to give therapy without falling back on these ideas.

On these training courses dozens of people have watched me work with patients, scores have analysed my questioning methods and I have never been reproached with 'leading' a patient in any particular direction. I know that the patient is the only one with the key to their problem. It is my job to assist them to find that key, not persuade them to accept my ideas. Never amongst the many volunteer patients treated in front of trainees has anyone gone back into a 'past life' and it has happened only once out of an uncountable number of people treated in normal, private sessions. This person, a young man of about 23 believed, as I do, that it was just his imagination.

Under Hypnosis, if one is prepared to accept the suggestions given, it is possible to float around the room or fly over your town – in your own mind. It will feel real, it will appear real. To all intents and purposes it IS real – at the time. You will be able to hear the choir singing as you pass by the church steeple, you will be able to feel the rain on your face and the wind as it penetrates your clothes – while you are still lying relaxed on a comfortable chair in a warm room.

It is possible to experience any sensation from lying on the beach under the powerful rays of the warm sun, to the exhaustion caused by scaling a steep, high hill. All while still in the same chair.

The heights of euphoric happiness and the depths of darkest despair can be yours as can the caress of someones' hands or the terror of your hair on fire.

All these things can be 'real' to you. And I mean 'real'. The terror you experience when your hair is alight is genuine terror – so much so that you may bring yourself out of hypnosis to run for the water tap. The exhaustion when you get to the top of hill is genuine exhaustion – until you return from the relaxed state of hypnosis to full alertness.

Again I must repeat that you will experience these things only if you wish to, no-one can use hypnosis to make you. They can only suggest – and you will only experience these things if you decide to go along with these suggestions.

By relaxing the analytical part of your mind you have allowed direct access to the part that reacts. This part, your subconscious, reacts without analysis to whatever is put in it so long as it does not conflict with previous information. If your conscious mind allows the suggestion that your hair is on fire to by-pass it (and remember you can always reject anything that you do not like), then the subconscious has to accept the suggestion and will bring into play your automatic self-preservation processes and you will feel terror together with all the physical effects (heart, breathing etc.) necessary to get you out of danger.

Thus you can experience 'Astral Projection' just by accepting the suggestions of someone else, so it is obviously possible to do so following your own suggestions – which believers may call 'natural' or 'spontaneous'.

The fire you only felt because you already had knowledge of fire. Without this knowledge the word 'fire' would have been meaningless and you could not have had the same experience. You used your imagination to connect the fire with your hair and almost certainly had the acrid stench of burning hair in your nostrils as well.

Your imagination is a powerful force whether used for your benefit or to your detriment but it can only be used by someone else in this way if you are prepared to allow it to happen.

If the medicine man 'points the bones at you' as a signal that you will die, then die you almost certainly will if you believe in his power. But it is the power of your own imagination that has the effect, not of the voodoo. If you accept that you will die then you will create the reality. You will look for symptoms; you will act as if you were dying because you believe you are and thus you will create the symptoms. But if you think the man is a charlatan and his magic a load of mumbo-jumbo, then his curses can have no effect.

Again this is accepting, or rejecting suggestions. It is using your imagination just as those do who go back into 'past lives'. A little bit of a book, a little bit from the television, a tiny piece from the first history lesson at school all put together with a half-undertood item that dad read out of a newspaper when you were 4 years old all come together to create a fantasy. It appears to be as simple as that.

I am not making these comments lightly. I know many people have a firm conviction that their 'past lives' still influence them. I have always found this impossible to reconcile with free-will but years ago when the opportunity arose to investigate, I did so. A group of us, some of whom were firm believers in 'past lives' did a series of tests. Most of these proved negative and none gave any credibility to the 'past life' theory: a French maid in Paris in the 17th century not only could speak no word of the French language but wasn't even certain if her name was Annette or Antoinette!

Another lady brought up the name of a village in Kent and the name of the Squire and his Lady who lived at the "big house". My researches were unable to turn up anything about the place or the people even when going through details of surrounding counties. Yet this was recent history, the period she was talking about was only just over lOO years ago and would thus have been well documented.

To me, however, the most interesting case was a man who believed he was a magistrate taking a woman to the debtors prison in a coach. While I watched and listened to the person guiding him through the experience I was sitting next to his wife who whispered to me that she found it fascinating that in this life he still had the same three great hates as in his previous existence – paper work, travelling and debts. To her it was confirmation of a previous existence, to me it was just the opposite – he couldn't change his nature even when fantasising.

A completely different interpretation from the same information.

But the deciding factor for me was when he mentioned that the woman in his charge was 'handcuffed'. Handcuffs were not invented for many years after the time in which he 'lived'. She could have been tied but there was no way that she could have been handcuffed.

One of the ladies showed no physical response to questioning while relaxed, and when she was afterwards asked why she had neither moved nor spoken replied "I couldn't, I was a tree"!

When in the relaxed state we call hypnosis you can recapture the taste of the jelly at your third birthday party or the smell of the heather on your first trip to the mountains. Your imagination can make all these 'real' to you – but it is still only your imagination.

Again I wish to refer to events on my training courses and I do this for two reasons. When training people it is sometimes necessary to demonstrate why certain techniques should not be employed in therapy and thus it is only during training that I would ever use some of the things that I describe.

The second reason is that these incidents have taken place in front of a group of witnesses some of whom are very analytical. These people are paying their hard-earned cash to find out and will question, they will interrogate, they will ask for proof. They are going to become professional Hypnotherapists and they want to know. Some of them have travelled a long way – not just from all parts of the United Kingdom but from Malta, Nigeria, Israel and South Africa as well as other overseas areas. Some of those from abroad have had to resign from lucrative employment to come on the course and they know that, once they are back in their own country, they will have to rely on themselves to a very large extent. They must, therefore, get every possible bit of information and understanding that they can while they are in Birmingham.

Can anyone do more than prove things in front of a room full of analytical and critical witnesses?

One trainee said that he felt cold and we (i.e. he and myself together) therefore induced hypnosis and made him feel warm. When he came out of his relaxed state the first thing he did was to wipe sweat from his brow and a doctor who was on the same course commented that it had been interesting to watch his physiological reactions.

When I asked him to tell us what he had seen he replied that he had watched the volunteers hands turn from blue to red.

On another course one of the participants turned up one Saturday with a really bad attack of influenza. Aching legs, pains in his back and head, a sore throat, having difficulty in keeping his eyes open and looking as if he would not last out the day.

Obviously we could not get rid of 'flu but we could certainly ease his symptoms and enable his natural protective processes to fight the virus more effectively. We therefore did so and also got rid of his aches and pains – but the other thing we did was more interesting.

Having checked that he liked the flavour, we made his saliva taste like honey to soothe his throat. When we stopped for lunch he got a cup of his usual drink (black coffee, no sugar) from the vender and was unable to drink it because it was too sweet! The following morning he told me that I had ruined his breakfast for the the same reason. However, this was not a complaint as he considered coffee deprivation better than his sore throat.

So what had we really done with these people? We had simply enabled them to use their imagination to create a physical change in themselves – but a real change. The colour change in the one person's hands was visible, as was the perspiration on his forehead. The taste of honey was a genuine taste which the other person kept until his sore throat had eased away a few days later.

But I did not do it. I simply enabled them to do it for themselves and they created a genuine physical effect in themselves out of their imagination.

On another course one of the trainees called me a 'healer' as I completed treatment of a volunteer with a painful back from which she had suffered for years. I find this sort of description annoying – I have never healed anyone. All I ever do is enable them to heal themselves by correcting whatever is in their mind creating their problem.

The taste of honey and the warmth were 'real' to these people just as the 'past lives' that other people conjure up are 'real'. Just as astral projection is 'real' to others. As 'real' as the death that the medicine man can get YOU to bring about if you accept his suggestion and use your imagination as he wishes. As real as the effects of the love potion that you may give to someone you desire. If you believe in its power it will not only make you look for signs that your love is returned but give you the confidence to pursue the object of your desire with added vigour thus possibly ensuring success when you thought you were previously failing; and, of course, if the recipient of the potion knew it had been administered, and believed in its efficacy, he or she would 'know' that they were automatically in love with the giver – making the outcome a foregone conclusion, and creating a genuine reality out of their imaginations.

If one can create actual physical warmth in their body; if one can change the taste in their mouth, if one can ease away aches and pains simply with the power of their own mind, is it such a big step to believing that the mind holds the key to many physical problems?

I would like to end this chapter by repeating that you will only accept under hypnosis what you wish to accept. If you don't want to imagine that your hair is on fire – then you won't. If you are prepared to allow it to happen just a bit, then you will be able to stop it there, or even come out of hypnosis when that stage is reached. No one controls you, no one can make you do anything you do not wish nor get you to experience anything that you do not want to.

You will always have control.

"What makes you think that my problem stems from a past life"

Makers, Pushers, Poppers
and Failures

Around the world there are many people who make their living by
isolating and correcting wrong information in office computers but
pitifully few who do the same job when data in our personal
computer - our sub-conscious mind - is at fault.

The main efforts of therapists are directed towards suppressing
symptoms - painkillers for persistent headaches, without trying to
find their cause. Sedatives for anxiety, without trying to find out
why. Even attempts to jolt the brain to temporarily give up
depression by the brute force of electro-convulsive 'therapy'.

We suppress the symptom of hay fever with anti-histamine. We fit
maskers to over-ride noise in the heads of those who suffer continual
ringing in the ears (tinnitus). We have sleeping pills for those with
insomnia, tranquilisers for those with anxiety, inhalers for
asthmatics. We have the acupuncturists needles to attempt correction
of 'energy flows' or help overcome pain. We have allergy clinics to
take people off food that is tasty, nutritious and beneficial to the bulk
of the population

All these are useful; anything that helps relieve suffering has its
place; yet none of these things can get at the cause of a problem, and
it is only by uncovering the cause that a cure can be obtained.

Every day our population consumes tonnes of pills, we pop them into
our mouths by the million — and millions of ££s are spent on
developing new drugs, yet how much is spent in investigation of why
patients have their problems?

The Daily News on 16th August 1989 stated that, in Birmingham
alone, half of all those people who turned to a drug helpline in a bid
to quit drug addiction are people who want to quit taking
tranquilisers. They quoted the number of annual prescriptions in
England and Wales at more than 25 million and estimated that 3
million people could be hooked — that is one in twenty of the
population.

Think of it! A vast number of people who have been on these drugs
for years and years. How many more have started taking these pills
during that period? The actual figure of those who are now
tranquiliser addicts must be astronomical.

There is no good blaming the doctors who prescribe these pills. They are doing their best within the confines of their training, the sales blurbs of the drug companies and the financial constraints of their patients who get their drugs on the National Health Service with little cost and would have to pay for curative treatment. (Although one gets numerous cases like the patient who came at the suggestion of her doctor and told me that she had spent far more in prescription fees for painkillers and in dental 'gags' in attempts to reduce her face pain over an eleven year period, than she paid me to enable her to cure her problem in about a month even after allowing the expense of travelling 50 miles for treatment).

There is no good blaming the drug companies either. Although they have made some ghastly and heartbreaking errors in the drugs they release onto the public, they are commercial concerns and have to do their best to sell a product if they believe in it, otherwise they could not exist. They do their work to the best of their ability and their products have, in many cases, alleviated problems or saved lives.

We certainly cannot put the blame on the patients themselves. They go to experts and believe they are getting the best treatment available - what else can a non-technical person do?

We have to blame 'The System'. Not just the National Health Service (which is at last showing a tiny interest in Curative methods of hypnosis) but the whole of the system which makes the average person regard their medical practitioner - and through them, the drug companies - as if they are infallible and appears to make many doctors feel the same way.

The system that breeds people with closed minds. Minds that are unable to accept new ideas or even a new approach to an established one.

I cannot change this system - the question is: can the public? I believe that they not only can, I firmly believe that they will and their greater acceptance of all sorts of 'alternative' medicines could force proper investigation.

But let us go back to the pill-makers, the pill-pushers and the pill-poppers and ask a simple question:

Why do these tranquilisers become ineffective after 4 months?

A simple question for which I do not have a simple answer because I do not have the facilities to do the research necessary. But I do have an answer which fits a large number of people who have come to me for treatment:

Those for whom these pills were prescribed had a logical reason for their anxiety, depression or whatever. The pills were purely a symptom supressant, and gradually the 'need' for their anxiety overcame the power of the drug.

What does a Curative Hypnotherapist do when a patient attends for treatment with a note from their medical practioner asking whether he can help a lady to give up anti-depressant drugs or tranquilisers without suffering withdrawal symptoms? (I am talking now about a person who knows how to use Curative Hypnotherapy – not just a hypnotherapist).

The answer to this one is simple indeed. Our therapist will use his best endeavours to enable the lady to recall the reason why she needed the drug in the first place. When that is corrected the drug is redundant and gradual withdrawal can take place without difficulty.

Of course, our therapist could use **Curative methods** to do exactly what the doctor has requested and deal with the reason for the withdrawal symptoms but this would almost inevitably lead back to the same incident – the one that first started her on the path to developing her problem.

When you consider that some people have been taking these pills for more than a quarter of a century and that many of them could have their problem corrected in a couple of months or so, does it not make the ecomomics of our health service look a little sick?

Notice that in the previous paragraph I use the expression "that most of them could have their problems corrected". Not, unfortunately, all of them. Every therapist has failures. My previous book had a whole chapter with this title but I still feel that a few words on the subject are called for here.

Failures fall into two main categories:

1. those who cease treatment before it has really got started
2. those with whom I call a halt in treatment.

The first category do not really give any therapist a chance. They will, apparently listen to what you have to say about hearing everything and understanding everything while in hypnosis yet, even though they may relax very well, they do not believe they were hypnotised. They still believe the fairy tales of hypnotic 'trances' and being controlled. Or if they are prepared to admit that they experienced something unusual they will say that they have not felt any real lasting benefit – after just one treatment! Again they have not listened to the therapists' explanations and have a belief that hypnosis is a magic cure-all.

When a therapist gives these explanations at the initial consultation, before commencing hypnosis, he does his best but he cannot deal with closed minds. If people are not prepared to believe that their therapist has more experience in the use of hypnosis than they have – well, you cannot talk for hours. In my own practice there has always been a small percentage who do not come back after the first or second treatment.

Those who do return will normally follow through the treatment to a successful conclusion but there are still the people in category 2 who can be split into two further types:

2a. Those who know best! who will insist on doing their own therapy. They have no knowledge or understanding of hypnosis – if they had they would know that the only way to speed the treatment is to accept. Not to analyse, not to use their intelligence, not to interfere with the treatment – but to accept. They will accept hypnosis otherwise we would not have got past their second treatment but will not accept anything further. They are the people who insist that they cannot stop analysing, that they have an analytic mind, that they are "complex individuals" (isn't everyone?) They waste time which I could be devoting to helping a more genuine person. These time-wasters, luckily, form a very small proportion of those who come for treatment and, as you will have gathered, I have no patience with them.

2b. This is the category that really hurts me. Those who go along with the treatment beautifully but whose cases I am still unable to 'crack' because of my own mental limitations. In many of these cases, a fresh mind will do the trick. An alternative approach, a different way of expressing things may find the key that I lack. I then suggest that these people may like to try another Curative Hypnotherapist and, of course, I sometimes get patients who have been referred by my colleagues who have been experiencing the same sort of difficulty. Usually, these people are fairly straightforward to treat successfully – not because I am clever but because I am me. I am different, just as everyone else is different. Although the basic methods of Curative Hypnotherapy have to be the same, the way each therapist expresses him or herself and puts the methods into practice has to be their own individual way.

Thankfully, the majority of those who come for therapy are outside these categories and together we are normally able to reach our goal.

One lovely lady of 63 years was almost in the last category. Her major problem was anxiety. She went along beautifully with the treatment on her first couple of visits and I had intimated to her that I thought about another five sessions would be all that was necessary. But then we started floundering and eventually reached the ninth session. Then the breakthrough, or so I thought, in a letter she sent from which I quote verbatim:

"Dear Mr. Lesser,

When I visited you last Tuesday you said that my father would say something to me and I couldn't hear anything at all

As my father was a very quiet man and my mother was the talkative person I could not understand this.

On Thursday evening I was at my daughters house playing with my grandchildren when suddenly I could quickly see the shop where I was born and lived with my parents and grandparents until we moved when I think I was 5 or 6, maybe only 4 years old. I'm not sure of the age.

When I saw our shop last it was about 2 years ago and it was very delapidated. It was a large shop with 14 rooms.

When I visualised the shop on Thursday it was as I was when young – the windows full of light and sweet bottles etc. in the windows and I was standing there with my friend Mary ————— just outside the front door.

A young man came up to us, I don't know what he looked like but I know he exposed himself to us. We were afraid but didn't know what to do and he made us touch him. I know that we were both terrified but unable to know what to do.

The next thing I know of this horrible affair was when my father was holding me up in his arms in the Court, I presume so that the people could see me but I don't remember seeing them, but I can remember being told to point to the man which I presume I did but I don't remember doing so.

I can remember my parents being very distressed but didn't really know what was going on.

I think this is all I can remember but I do hope when I see you it will help you to sort out my problems.

sincerely –

Sometimes, as you disturb old memories, a person will recall further events in between treatments. It is fairly unusual and it is certainly a waste of time for people to sit and try to think. However, it is nice when somebody's sub-conscious does some of the work for the therapist: So we took up the contents of her letter which she said she would not have been able to tell any therapist previously (even had she remembered the incident) because of her distaste of everything sexual. She still had her distaste but was at least able to talk about her dislike and agreed that she knew it was an unnatural reaction.

But we made no progress for the next four sessions and on two occasions I suggested that she might try a different mind on her problem by going to another practioner of Curative Hypnotherapy. Both times she refused to even consider a change of therapist and I felt we were so near the truth that I continued trying.

Then came the real breakthrough in the form of a further letter:

> *"Dear Mr. Lesser,*
>
> *Excuse writing I want to drop you this line and I am in a hurry.*
>
> *When I saw you last you said that I would hear a voice telling me a name, but as usual with me I could hear no name, but the following day when I was at my daughters house suddenly I saw the shop where I was born and Mary ——— (you know that name by now) and I were in her back yard and playing then we went to the toilet at the end of the yard and we were touching each other between our legs. I know I felt awful about doing it even though I was only 4 years old and it was all so nasty to me when I saw it last week. It really upset me. I can see that doing this was to me an awful thing to do, though maybe more so to me because of my father being such a strict person and maybe I also am or was a very narrow minded child, though I don't know how to put it but I still feel I was doing wrong.*
>
> *Fancy this coming back after all these years. We can talk it out on Wednesday."*

(The wording and punctuation are exactly as in the original hurried notes from my patient apart from the change in the name of her friend to ensure complete anonimity).

This natural bit of childish exploration was what lay at the root of her problem. Once we had that we soon found out how words by her mother, together with that incident had created her anxiety and also, of course, her complete lack of any sexual feeling.

It took us 14 sessions to get rid of her anxiety. Far longer than the average length of treatment because she had not been prepared to admit to anything sexual – either consciously or sub-consciously – her distaste for sex had been too great. The logical progression from being made to touch a young man to the creation of her anxiety was, however, missing and I had to keep searching.

The really interesting aspect of this case is the way that, even after she was prepared to dredge up something sexual (and this was not following any suggestion of mine, but came first in her letter) she had to turn it into something more acceptable, more palatable to her than the truth.

The man; the court case; being held up to identify her 'abuser'; all these were complete fantasy. It was more acceptable to her to touch a man than a girl. There was less violation in touching than being touched. It was more acceptable to be forced to do so than to do it voluntarily, and it is obviously more acceptable that the person doing the forcing is an adult rather than a child.

Having created the fantasy she then filled in the picture further to create greater credibilty for herself (not for me) by adding the court case.

Yet when she wrote her first letter and when we talked, she really believed that the incident with the man had taken place and I believed her as well. Did you notice, however, that in both of her letters the incidents (both true and false) occurred to her when she was at her daughter's house? For a reason she could not explain, this was important enough for her to put in both letters. After the second letter she told me that this memory, too, had come back while playing with her grandchildren. You, of course, can see why – her grandchilren were 4 and 5 years old!

This lady was what I would call a 'near failure'. I could so easily have ceased treating her because I felt we were making no progress.

Think how easy it would have been for a therapist to accept her story of the mythical 'flasher'. But there was no logicality to this story although I must admit that I believed it and was expecting to find something else that she had put with that incident to create her problem. The contents of her second letter came like a bolt from the blue, although in this therapy one should not really be surprised by anything.

As a matter of interest this lady had been on tranquilisers for many years. She gave them up before we spent our final session together making sure there was nothing that could cause anxiety in the future, nor the pains in her shoulders and groin and nothing to prevent a normal sleeping pattern from now on.

We also took the opportunity to deal with any hindrances to sexual satisfaction and when she left for the last time her words were: "I have fifty years to make up for".

I'm still waiting for her husband to come for virility treatment!!

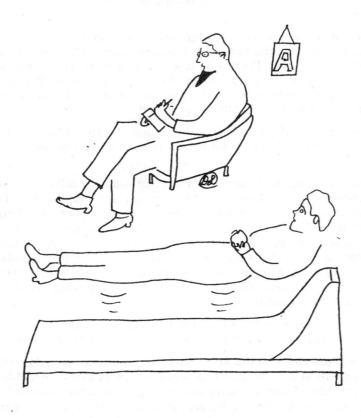

"My doctor says it's all done by relaxation"

Transference, Rapport and Body Language

Some therapists place great store in quasi-scientific jargon (i.e. transference, hypnogogic, rapport, trance, hypnopompic, altered state of consciousness [altered to what? altered from what?] and so on) to add to the mystique they seem to believe necessary, and gradually these words have been used to encompass additional meanings.

Rapport, for instance, is simply the establishment of communication. Yet a few years ago I read in a book on hypnosis that if a therapist left the room while they had a patient in relaxation then "rapport would be broken" and the patient would immediately come out of their relaxed state.

Obviously this writer believed (or maybe just **wanted** to believe) that he had some mysterious power which, I assume, would not pass through walls! But think about it; the patient had achieved the relaxed state that we call hypnosis simply by going along with the suggestions made by the therapist. So it would be the easiest thing in the world for him to accept a further suggestion such as "I'm leaving the room for a couple of minutes, so, while I'm away just allow yourself to relax more deeply and when I return you'll be much more relaxed than you are now".

Although I dislike breaking my concentration while working with a patient I have used words similar to these on a few occasions in the past and everyone has always accepted them. No one has rejected the suggestion, yet everyone has had the ability to do so.

Unless there was a real emergency, my staff would never allow me to be disturbed while I am giving treatment but many Hypnotherapists, when starting in practice, do not have a receptionist and could be disturbed by the ringing of their door bell. I would hope, however, that this would be an infrequent occurrence. They should be able to organise their appointments to avoid this apart from a few exceptional cases.

There is one occasion that stands out in my mind on the subject of 'rapport'. A girl of about 23 came for treatment for her fear of dogs. This fear had become so acute that she had reached the stage where she had almost decided that she could no longer face going to work and for the last few months had not left her home in the evenings or at weekends, even to visit friends. A dog securely tethered on the other side of the road was enough to cause palpitations, breathlessness and stomach churning with her legs turning to jelly.

On the occasion of which I am now writing she was the last patient of the day and as it was well into the evening and no further callers were expected, my staff put on the answering machine to take care of any 'phone callers and then went home.

She had relaxed into hypnosis when there came a ring on the door bell. I ignored it hoping the caller would go away but on the third ring decided I would have to answer. I told my patient to ". . . just relax until I return" and went out to attend to the visitor. Three or four minutes later I returned to my room and just took up the treatment at the point we had left and continued the session to the end without any difficulties whatsoever, although I noticed there had been a considerable change in her breathing rate while I had been away.

This was her third treatment so one would have assumed that whatever 'rapport' was likely to be established was already in existence. However, before she left that evening she told me that when I had gone out of the room she had the fear that I had gone out to bring in a dog with which to confront her. She knew my methods of treatment. On more than one occasion I had talked about finding the cause of her fear. We were well into the treatment. She was responding well. She knew and fully understood what we were doing, yet still she had this distrust. So had we really established this mysterious thing called 'rapport'?

She was an intelligent girl and had read of the 'de-sensitizing' procedures used by some psychiatrists whereby they expose patients to the things or situations which were causing their fears – for instance a person with a fear of spiders may be exposed to a spider in a glass box at the other side of the room, then gradually it is brought nearer, then tipped out of the box onto a table near the patient and so on. She knew that this process is normally done over a considerable period and, more importantly, knew that I disagreed with this method of treatment as it still left the CAUSE of the problem untouched to show itself, possibly in a different and more distressing way, in the future.

The reason she had chosen myself as a therapist rather than the psychiatrist suggested by her doctor was that she had read some articles that I had been asked to write for various publications and fully understood that my methods were completely different. Yet she still had this mistrust.

So how strong was this thing called 'rapport' between us?

'Rapport' is simply establishment of communication, and communication is certainly a requirement for Hypnotherapy. But one does not need anything except the normal communication between two people to be successful. Some people have a belief that a Hypnotherapist must put on some sort of show of being a charismatic figure and reflect this in their mode of dress. Others believe that the decor of their working place will make the difference between success and failure. In reality, however, the important thing is: will that individual accept your suggestions. It is genuinely as simple as that.

Years ago I gave treatment to a woman whose son brought her up from the South coast. He rang on a Saturday and said it was an emergency as she was determined to kill herself. I normally see no patients at the weekend as I work up to 12 hours a day during the week and need time to pay my bills and do the background work necessary for the running of a practice as well as time for things like the writing of this book and running my weekend training courses, apart from taking some time off work. However, this man sounded so urgent that I could not turn him down.

It is not possible to get my room decorated by professionals during the week because of the constant flow of people needing treatment, and painters and decorators are not often keen to work weekends. So I was in the middle of painting my room when he rang and although I had 4 or 5 hours notice of their arrival while they covered the distance to Birmingham I was still painting when they arrived. I greeted them dressed in a pair of old trousers with a hole where my bunch of keys had worn through. I had paint on my trousers, my hands and, he later pointed out, in my hair, with a smear or two on my face. My room looked as though a tornado had hit it. All the furniture was piled on one side with files and documents all over the place, while the cleared part of the room was freshly painted with the paint still wet. The place was a mess, I was a mess, and the smell of paint was almost overpowering. Yet she was still prepared to accept. I must have looked like a tramp yet still she accepted. And she accepted because she wanted to and for no other reason.

If you wish to use words like 'rapport' – she had already established this before she even entered my premises. It had nothing to do with my appearance, my personality, or my premises. Had she felt, even after that long drive and the trouble her son was taking, that she could not have trusted me then she would not have accepted treatment from me, but I gave no reason for distrust and this is really the core of the relationship between therapist and patient.

On more than one occasion in the past, new patients have expressed doubts about whether they can be hypnotised. Sometimes they have gone through a failed session of hypnosis and been told by their 'therapist' that they are one of the 10% (or 20% or some other percentage according to what books that particular 'therapist' has read) that cannot be hypnotised. Remarks like these are just an excuse by the therapist. Everyone can be hypnotised. All it needs is a lack of mistrust and a method which that particular patient finds suitable. In other words – acceptance.

I have even had more than one person who was told when in relaxation, that they would accept hypnosis from no other 'therapist' – and a more disgusting way of trying to keep patients I can hardly conceive.

These people normally accept hypnosis very easily at the first session with me in spite of this post-hypnotic suggestion. The mere fact that they come to me for treatment means that they have rejected this suggestion already.

On the other hand, during a talk I gave to a group of about 40 people, one of the questions put to me made me decide to demonstrate the ease with which suggestions can be accepted. I told the audience that I had no intention of attempting to induce hypnosis. Simply to demonstrate that anyone and everyone could accept suggestions.

One man came up to me afterwards and apologised for not going along with the demonstration. He explained that he had once experienced hypnosis and the hypnotist had instructed him that he would be unable to accept hypnosis from anyone else.

Therefore, he 'knew' he could not go along with the demonstration.

I pointed out to him that the only reason he could not accept was because he **believed** he could not. However, my quick explanation (there was a crowd of people waiting with further questions) fell on deaf ears.

He was a classic case of acceptance of suggestions from the wrong kind of person. Yet in rejecting my demonstration he was showing his **complete acceptance** of the previous suggestion.

In reality he was just refusing to go along with me and the other 39 present, and a longer chat with him would probably have enabled him to understand.

Hypnosis is achieved by accepting suggestions and all of us accept all sorts of suggestions every day. We accept them from our family, our friends, our workmates and from advertisers who persuade us, by suggestion, that their particular product is better than an alternative. But we all accept different suggestions in varying ways otherwise we would all be eating the same breakfast cereal and there would only be one brand of detergent on the market.

We accept suggestions that make us observe the law of the land. Putting aside morals for the moment, there is no physical force that prevents us shop-lifting, there is only the acceptance that we stand a good chance of being caught and punished, and we also accept that, if apprehended and taken to court, we would have difficulty in facing the shame involved.

So, everyone accepts suggestions and thus everyone can be hypnotised. But it is unlikely that anyone will accept relaxation from someone that they distrust. This applies particularly before they have experienced hypnosis and have not realised that they are still conscious and awake and able to reject anything that does not suit them.

I point out these facts to those who have doubts about their ability to be hypnotised and tell them that it isn't necessary for them to like me. It does not even matter if they actually dislike me. It does not matter whether I like them or not (of course I get some people that I actively dislike but the success rate remains the same). All that is necessary is a sufficient lack of mistrust. And that sums up the mysterious 'rapport'.

Trust also plays a part in 'body language' which some therapists believe is an aid to them in therapy. For instance, let us assume that a lady comes into my room and sits down in the reclining chair that they will be using during treatment. She sits on the edge of the chair and does not look too comfortable. Is this because she does not trust me and is ready to get up and run from the room or is it because she is a small woman and if she sits well back in the chair her feet will no longer touch the ground, which would be uncomfortable for her? Does it mean she trusts me but has a fear of hypnosis or could it be that she has a bad back and can only ease it by sitting ramrod straight?

If she puts her bag on the floor on my side of her chair is she showing her trust of me or building a barrier between us? If she puts it the other side of the chair is this mistrust or removal of barriers – complete trust? Remember, she has to either clutch it (distrust?) or put it somewhere.

It is generally accepted by those who subscribe to the theories of 'body language' that to cross your arms or legs while talking to someone means that you are not fully accepting what they are saying. Yet so much depends on physical feelings, aches, pains, stiffness, etc and on the chair itself. The height of a chair, the size of the seat all make a difference to that person's balance and could almost necessitate a crossing of the legs and once the legs are crossed it is quite natural to cross your arms as well.

In an advertisement inserted by the British Airports Authority in the Observer (23rd. Oct.1988) the 'manwatcher' Desmond Morris points out that pulling ones earlobe has 5 different meaning in 5 different countries – yet I know of people who tug their earlobes when deep in thought. Other examples of differing meanings for gestures were also given and Hans & Michael Eysenck in their book "Mindwatching" (Prion) quoted a psychologist who spent an hour watching couples in cafes in London, Puerto Rico and Paris. Apparently the Puerto Ricans touched each other 180 times, the French only 100 times while the British did not touch each other at all.

In "Cultural Misunderstandings: The French-American Experience", Raymonde Carrol of Oberlin College lists many differences in the ways that French and American people react to identical situations. French people "express their extreme anger with silence and lack of physical contact, the Americans just the reverse" i.e. shouting, and hitting. These differences do not just show up when comparing one continent to another but are obvious between neighbouring countries and even in different regions of the same country.

Not only do these 'mannerisms' vary from country to country and region to region but many are sub-consciously copied from parents, teachers and workmates and thus can give a therapist no real guide in serious therapy.

Can a therapist really tell whether posture, gestures or movements are conscious, sub-conscious or simply the response to an itch or the need to go to the lavatory? And while a therapist is looking for these signs and putting 'meanings' to them they are obviously not concentrating on their proper job. Of course facial expressions, in particular, can give a rough guide to the feelings that a person is experiencing at any instant but even these may be a long way from accurate unless the therapist knows how that person uses their facial muscles in all sorts of situations.

To use such 'signs' in therapy can be very misleading because the interpretation of them is that of the therapist not of the patient. This may very easily get in the way of understanding the interpretation that the patient has put on an event.

Therapists should beware of using artificial 'aids' such as body language because they can lead them very badly astray and patients should beware of therapists who use artificial 'aids' such as personality tests.

A person with a problem, a person who needs help and goes to someone they think is an expert can be easily 'blinded by science'. They rely on the expertise of the therapist yet a therapist who makes use of 'personality tests' or similar gimmicks is highly unlikely to have a proper understanding of how to uncover and correct the cause of a person's problem.

Everybody's problems are caused by a unique interpretation of events. Everybody reacts in accordance with past experiences and no two people have ever had identical experiences. To try to classify people into certain types is not going to help find out the incident that is creating the problem they wish to have solved. All these tests can do is point the therapist's mind in a particular direction which has to prevent him finding out the unique path of logic which the patient has followed.

I have done no research into these various tests so am not prepared to comment on how accurate they may be in defining a person's personality, but I do know that a therapist will get all sorts of personalities who come for treatment for a lack of confidence; with a weight problem or other complaint. The variation in personalities of people with similar problems is vast, and the only thing a proper Hypnotherapist should be interested in is exactly how that individual has created their problem. These tests play no part in this investigative process.

There is also a belief amongst some people who use hypnosis that what is called 'transference' has to take place. That the patient has to go through a series of differing emotions towards their therapist. They should love them, then hate them, then like them, then feel guilty about them.

Some even set out to create these emotions irrespective of the discomfort of the patient. All I ask from my patients is that they accept. Their feelings towards me should be a matter of complete indifference to me and to them as well. During treatment I want to be looked upon as a therapist not as a person — in that lies the speed of their cure. As long as they have that sufficient lack of mistrust to go along with my suggestions, then we will almost certainly succeed. That trust needs to be in my ability as a Hypnotherapist not in my personality. There are people that may dislike me and I am human enough to hope that some may even like me as a person not just as a therapist, but all that is incidental to the therapy.

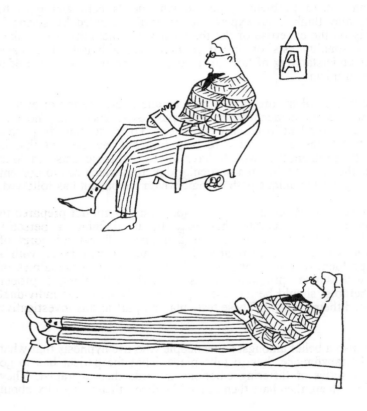

"What's all this about transference?"

Hypnosis and the Media

"FEARS FOR PUPILS IN A TRANCE" blared the banner headlines on the front page of the Sunday Mercury which covers the central part of England (7th.Feb.1988).

The article mentioned hypnosis being used with children who were

* refusing to go to school
* being confused or scatterbrained
* being noisy or troublesome in class
* suffering from nerves at exam times

and was followed on the Monday morning with telephone calls from national newspapers, television and radio who wanted to interview children whom I had treated for similar problems. When I informed them that what went on during treatment was confidential and I could not give them names, addresses or telephone numbers of patients, some tried to persuade me that I would not be breaking a confidence if I gave them the telephone numbers of the parents of my patients!

I offered to write to half a dozen parents asking if they and their offspring would co-operate with these reporters but, of course, this was useless for them – immediacy is the necessity for news. Stale news is no longer news.

One radio station took a different attitude and invited me to their studio for an interview which turned out to be a three-way talk between myself, the interviewer and the headmaster of a school who had been quoted in the paper as saying: "I certainly would not like this kind of treatment to happen to any of the children in my school. It could be very risky. It may well be dangerous."

It is almost unbelievable how a person who is in charge of an establishment devoted to education, a person whose object in life should be to enable children to learn to think for themselves, can pronounce judgement on something on which he has no knowledge whatsoever. This complete ignorance of hypnosis came over very strongly on the radio. He had no idea of what hypnosis was, never mind how it could be used to enable people to achieve their full potential.

The following week the same newspaper printed letters from readers with comments such as "It is terrible to use hypnotism on children" and ridiculous remarks about ". . . conditioned robots with pre-conditioned behaviour."

These people obviously had no knowledge or experience of hypnosis and, judging from the remarks they made, they had no intention of finding out. Their minds were completely closed.

I would ask these people why they should deny a child (or adult) the right to make the best of themselves and their lives. If a child has a hearing defect and has difficulty in understanding their teacher, would they refuse them the opportunity of remedial treatment? What is so different between this and the inabilty to concentrate? Both problems mean the child is being unnaturally held back in learning and both must have a cause.

At least the newspaper in its editorial, although very cautious indeed, said that education experts, and the wide range of remedial and child-psychology services that are already available would "do well to examine just why they have failed to convince some parents that they can be effective."

The answer to that question is, of course, that they are trying to tackle the problem by dealing with the computer-operator and ignoring the wrong data in the child's computer to which access can only be obtained by the use of hypnosis.

Immediacy is only one of the requirements that the news media require – the other is sensation.

Under the Headline " 'Zombie' boss wept at work" the Star newspaper reported that a businessman "often arrived at work in a daze after treatment from a hypnotist." However a later report did not mention hypnosis and only talked about this man having "**more than 2,500 injections** of a mysterious drug" from a doctor. Drugs are commonplace; hypnosis is news. The first newspaper article made no mention of any drug but went for the greater sensation and it is this first impression with which people are left.

Newspapers, radio and the most powerful medium of all – television; they all go for sensationalism – that is what sells; and television has the greatest effect because it impinges on two senses, sight and hearing, yet by its nature gives the viewer no chance of really thinking about what they have seen and heard. With a newspaper a person can read again, they can think, they can check back, but no-one records everything they watch on television so there is no opportunity for proper consideration, and first impressions have to be accepted once again.

In the Autumn of 1988 Central Television rang me to ask if they could send someone to get background information in connection with a forthcoming programme in which they were linking-up live with the

Russian town of Kiev. They intended to interview a Russian doctor who had, apparently, made advances in the use of hypnosis.

When the lady researcher who visited me told me that this man was using hypnosis to enable women to have breast operations without anaesthetic or pain, I informed her that this was nothing new. More than a century ago one doctor did hundreds of operations in this way. She then informed me that this man was different – he was using 'distant hypnosis'.

All that this meant was that he was using a television link between himself and the operating theatre. The programme was something of a farce in spite of it being introduced as "the sensation of this year". The doctor was little more than a stage hypnotist. He assured the viewers that he had been a doctor for 26 years but how many doctors would unexpectedly strike unsuspecting people on the forehead so that they crashed onto the floor on their backs?

The build-up was sensational as well – "I wonder if the doctor can give us a demonstration of some of his powers . . ." What power did he have? The ability to prevent pain, whether for an operation or to push a 6-inch nail right through a person's hand, lies within each individual. All the doctor demonstrated was that he could get a small number of people to accept his suggestions.

British and Russian doctors in the audience both in Kiev and Birmingham called his tricks 'unethical' yet hypnosis in the right hands is a powerful tool in the medical field and should not be brought down to the vaudeville level – least of all by a doctor.

A bogus doctor was the subject of an investigation on Channel 4 on 31st. January 1989. The programme was started by introducing him as "a con-man who has been using hypnosis to sexually abuse vulnerable women". Two cases were mentioned but no evidence to substantiate this phrase was produced.

Let me make it plain that I am not trying to 'whitewash' this man who had, according to the presenter of the programme, previously operated a fake charity.

My only interest is in the misrepresentation of hypnosis and the twisted half truths in which the media sometimes (far too often) become involved. This man, almost certainly, was not a genuine hypnotherapist but did he really use hypnosis to sexually abuse his female patients? After all, that was the point of the programme. It was not broadcast because of the sexual abuse but because he had been "using hypnosis" to achieve his aim.

The following is a precisely accurate report of what the one lady said:

"He . . . sat on the edge of the bed and the next thing I knew he was on top of me and I was pushing him and I said 'no . . . no . . .' . . . and he said 'why not?' . . . So I said 'because I don't want to,' . . . and he said 'you know you want to' . . . so I said 'no I don't.' . . . and that was it . . . He didn't remove my clothes. That was it . . . It's not like sex with someone you care for – he did it and I didn't want him to do it".

Come on, Channel 4! Where is the evidence of hypnosis? You categorically state that hypnosis can be used for seduction, you imply that a person in this state of relaxation can be made to do something against their will. Show us how this woman was controlled. She was in full possession of her faculties – she **knew** he sat on the bed, she **felt** him lie on top of her, she **pushed** him, she **argued** with him.

She was in control. She was able to use every form of defence that a person has, both physical and verbal. A case of rape – maybe. A case of straight forward seduction – maybe. A case of tricking someone into believing that intercourse was therapeutic – maybe. But misuse of hypnosis – it wasn't.

If you are saying that this woman was controlled by the hypnotist then she could not have argued and pushed him away. If she was not controlled – then she was willing.

A good con-man can convince many people of almost anything. The boss in the 'Zombie' case previously mentioned was persuaded to part with between £35,000 and £60,000 by his doctor for his 'mysterious drug'. One needs a glib tongue for this sort of thing – hypnosis will not do the trick.

The interviewer on this same television programme talked about hypnotherapists being "allowed to meddle with peoples' minds". Yet the only other 'evidence' produced was the story of a lady who was told to keep her eyes closed – and "on one occasion she opened them". So who had control? Not much evidence of the 'powers' of hypnosis in either of these cases and I feel it is more likely that his fake title of 'doctor' was what enabled him to get away with whatever really happened. But this would not have had such a sensational effect as the the use of the word 'hypnosis'.

Whether or not this man was a crook and a confidence trickster, this does not give any of the media the license to mis-represent hypnosis. In reality it was the television presenters who were "meddling with peoples' minds" with their mis-representation.

The end of this programme revealed the 'story at any price' attitude in which this programme was made – it showed the interviewer physically assaulting the accused man while he was surrounded by the cameramen and sound recording engineers. Maybe it was lucky for the interviewer that she was a woman! Or was she chosen for this job because there was less likelihood of a man who is assaulted defending himself properly against a female?

One fully appreciates that the news media need something that is newsworthy and I have always tried to co-operate when I have been asked to do a radio broadcast or talk to a newspaper or magazine reporter. I understand that these people must be right up to date with their topics. I'll talk on the air when it is rumoured that a member of the Royal family has a snake phobia or has lost excess weight through the use of hypnosis. With an experienced headmaster I'll argue the case for correctly using hypnosis to help kids overcome learning or behavourial difficulties. I do not really mind an interviewer poking fun as happened on the Royal snake phobia programme. But I do object to half-truths, to mis-representation, and to reporters or interviewers who go for sensation at no matter what cost to facts or truth.

I have to say that on those occasions that I have had contact with the media I have always been given a fair chance of putting the case for hypnotherapy bearing in mind the restrictions on time or space and the difficulty the uninitiated have in understanding our work, their natural cynicism and the need for a programme or article to be lively.

Because of ignorance about the subject and the mysticism that has been built up through the years, hypnotherapy is good for a cheap giggle and much of the literature about the subject does little to alleviate this situation.

There are so many books about hypnosis that someone wishing to find out about the subject would have difficulty knowing where to start. But it matters very little indeed. Most of these books are simply a re-hash of what has previously been written by another author. The cases may be different but the underlying philosophy is the same. You either suppress the symptom – temporarily; you teach them to live with their problem – for a time; or you try to get them to fit your particular theory – and then tell them they are cured; or persuade them to accept a substitute symptom.

I sometimes wonder whether those who profess to be experts on the subject have really given any thought to how they use hypnosis and to the content of their publications.

We have talked elsewhere about those with the peculiar oral, anal and genital theory and about one or two other authors and but may I now devote a couple of pages to brief notes on other writers:

"Hypnosis – A Gateway To Better Health" by Dr. Brian Roet (Weidenfeld & Nicholson). Chapter 2: Patient: Male. Problem: fear of driving. History: had a few drinks then nearly had a head-on collision on the way home. According to this author this is the reason for his patient's fear of driving. Yet thousands of people must have had actual collisions not just near misses without developing this phobia. Not only **no attempt to find out why** this man is reacting differently to others but the author actually admits that he believes the problem will re-surface if the man drinks and drives in the future.

Chapter 4. His method of dealing with worry is simply to put off non-urgent ones to the following day! Will not worry build on worry until a state of anxiety or another problem is created?

Page 54. A lady whose swallowing problem improved then reappered because **he had not found out why.**

Page 104. An overweight lady recalled her mother taking her to the doctor when she was 4 years old because she was fat. The author believed that it was the doctors' words on that occasion that is causing her weight problem. It does not take much commonsense to see that the cause of her weight problem has to be before the visit to the doctor as she was already fat on the occasion.

And what do you think about Dr. Roet saying that a therapist could lose contact with a patient under regression because, as a child, the patient spoke a different language, yet also talking about utilizing regression to the birth experience – a time when the patient would have no understanding of any language whatsoever? Would the therapist not automatically lose contact then? No matter how inexperienced or inept a therapist may be, I do not believe contact could be lost in the way he suggests – not even if the therapist deliberately tried to achieve this.

"The Theory and Practice of Hypnotism" by W.J.Ousby (Thorsons Publishers Ltd.) This author writes about "Hypnotherapy Clinics to which overworked doctors could send tense and worried patients to be taught how to relax . . ." he mentions group therapy and suggests that "people who are at present unable to receive psychological aid because of the shortage of therapists could receive reassurance through relaxation therapy pending psychiatric treatment".

He obviously knows that hypnosis is a state of relaxation but I can find nothing else in this book to demonstrate any further understanding than this. Hence his idea of using it only as a stop-gap.

"Hypnotherapy" by Dave Elman. (Westwood Publishing Co. Calif). We have mentioned this book previously but I feel that another case or two is called for:

Page 218. 11-year-old boy with asthma. Elman discovered that when the patient's sister was born the boy developed asthma to get his mothers attention. It apparently did not occur to this therapist that every elder child should be asthmatic according to his view. Further, his method of treatment could easily be a recipe for disaster. He got the parents to "do everything in their power to correct the brother and sister problem". Is this not giving their child a very good reason to hold onto his asthma in order to get his parents to do his bidding? Why not find out why this child needed attention so badly that he was damaging himself?

Page 230. A woman had depression "because" her mother committed suicide when she was 39 and the patient was nearing that age. Should we not ask ourselves why we don't all get depression when we near the age at which one of our parents die? Again and again, this inability to think and to ask WHY.

A final quote from this book: "In my opinion, every case of hay fever represents a crying syndrome". Obviously a pre-conceived idea that he intends to make the patient fit. Out of the countless cases of hay fever that I have successfully dealt with, I have never had a case of it being a 'crying syndrome' – but then, I know the patient is the only person who can possibly know the reason for this affliction and don't try to force them to fit my theories. Remember how the structure of the interview conducted by Mr. Elman with the woman suffering from dermatitis inevitably led to a pre-conceived conclusion of his own that her problem was caused by guilt. ("That's the term I'm hitting at . . .").

The purpose of these last couple of pages is to persuade people to THINK when reading about this subject. To analyse and to look for the inconsistencies. There has been so much uninformed writing on the subject of hypnosis, mainly because these writers build on the mistaken ideas of previous authors. They learn wrongly and thus pass on that learning without really using their minds on the subject. I have amassed enough notes similar to the above to fill page after page and, while I do not wish to bore the reader too much, I feel that a few more quotations may be pertinent.

Although written as recently as 1979, "Origins of the Mind" (Charles Furst, Prentice-Hall Inc., Englecliffe, N.J.) still perpetuates the age-old myth: "The hypnotised person is subservient in thought and action to the will of the hypnotist," yet goes on to talk about the hypnotised person responding co-operatively to suggestions. If co-operation is a requirement then how is the person subservient to "the will of the hypnotist"?. If it requires the co-operation of the subject then who, in reality, has control?

"The Healing Power of Hypnotism" (Caroline & David Shreeve, Thorson Publishing Group P96): ". . . the true nature of the anxiety attack; it is a distorted way of releasing sexual energy which cannot be channeled in the normal way because this outlet has been denied to it". It would be interesting to know how they fit this pre-conceived idea to a person who turns to orgasm as a temporary relief from anxiety. Some anxiety sufferers, both male and female, turn to sexual intercourse (sometimes with dozens of partners) or become compulsive masturbators as the sexual feeling and release are the only things that can divert their minds away from their worries. But again, these authors follow the oral, anal & genital theory of making people fit into nice, neat compartments.

"The Use of Hypnosis in Psychopathia Sexualis" (A. von Schrenck-Notzing, **The Institute for Research in Hypnosis,** New York). I include this solely because of the name of the publisher. Originally published 100 years ago this book was republished as late as 1956 with a foreword by Henry Guze of the Department of Psychology, Long Island University who called it a "classic contribution". There may be an excuse for the original author's obsession with the size, shape and hirsute covering of the male and female genitalia and cranial and pelvic measurements, but in the sixty-one years that passed before the modern printing, one would have thought that an 'Institute for Research in Hypnosis' would not still be advocating "**suggestive** treatment in hypnosis" as being the "only means of salvation" (page 208). I would be most interested to know in what way this Institute conducts research.

There appears to be a never-ending list of books on the subject of hypnosis but those who wish to learn about the subject will never do so from reading the publications that are on the market as they are all variants on the theme of symptom suppression. Most certainly they will learn nothing useful from the occasional sensation in the news-media as the presenters talk from ignorance and their research is, in reality, non-existent.

None of the interviewers with whom I have had contact had any knowledge of hypnosis so I offered one, over the airwaves, the chance to experience this beautiful state of relaxation. He appeared to have absorbed considerable wrong information on the subject and to have a fear of being 'taken over'. His last words on the programme were "I'll take up your offer and I'll be in touch with you."

I scribbled him a note the same day confirming my offer but in spite of his promise which was heard by the listening public, there has been no contact. To have experienced would have been to know, and to know would have made him regard hypnosis seriously not just as a sensation or a joke.

POSTSCRIPT: Just before this book went to print I was asked to contribute to a BBC 2 programme on the subject of asthma, which was broadcast on June 9th.1989.

I have only taken part in live broadcasts previously as I realise how easily a recording can be edited to give a biased point of view. But I broke my golden rule on this occasion and agreed to go along with a recorded programme. In doing so I proved that my fears about editing are well-founded.

Just three-and-a-half minutes of this programme were on acupuncture and **only two-and-a-half minutes** devoted to Hypnotherapy. The rest of the **half hour** was all on the subject of orthodox symptom treatment. A Consultant chest physician (backed by illuminated chest X-rays) said there were only two lines of attack for asthma: 1) relieve symptoms (by which I assume he meant using an inhaler as this was the main thrust of the programme), or 2) using a preventative inhaler. No question of a cure here!

The announcer stated that asthma can come on suddenly at any age; but there was no suggestion of questioning what changes take place in a person to create it after years of asthma-free living.

There was mention of stress being a cause and an asthmatic Member of Parliament, Edwina Curry, said "tension can set it off". No thought that tension and stress are mental reactions and the answer to asthma must, therefore, lie in the mind.

A second doctor talked about 'alternative people' being 'quacks' and 'charlatans'. Even in the interests of his patients he did not appear to have the ability to look beyond the conventions of his professional training. No evidence whatsoever was produced to substantiate his remarks.

The doctor fronting the illuminated X-rays said that where alternatives to orthodox treatment have "been looked at, the changes have been very minor"; yet he also stated that "the trouble with all forms of non-conventional medicine is that there have been no real scientifically controlled studies of the efficacy of this treatment".

How can a person talk about only minor results unless there has been a proper study of the subject? Why has there been no proper study? I would have thought that this man was in a fairly good position to apply pressure in the proper place to get an investigation started.

My mind was not on the questions when the TV crew came to interview me as they had considerably over-run the time allotted and my major concern by then was a lady who had been waiting for half-an-hour for treatment. But this did not really make any difference. The interview with me was cut just as I was about to explain how I gave up suppressing symptoms and devoted myself to finding, then correcting, the cause.

This portrayed me as a self-confessed symptom-treater – a travesty of the truth.

The only enlightening thing to come out of this programme was almost certainly missed by the viewers as it was by me when I watched the original broadcast. It was only when I viewed a recording of the programme that I realised that only one person interviewed had been cured. Just one person out of all those who took part in the measuring of lung capacity and the use of inhalers. no longer suffered asthma. This was a lady interviewed in my reception area to whom I had given treatment a couple of years ago! **She had no symptom treatment from me then and she has needed no symptom treatment since.**

I do not believe that these TV producers deliberately set out to denigrate our work but they were most certainly under the influence of 'the establishment'. 80% of programme time was devoted to just one therapy and 20% shared between two others, and the therapy that actually cured being given the smallest allocation of time of them all. They obviously believed in 'playing it safe' and sticking to orthodox symptom treatment, paying only token lip-service to other therapies.

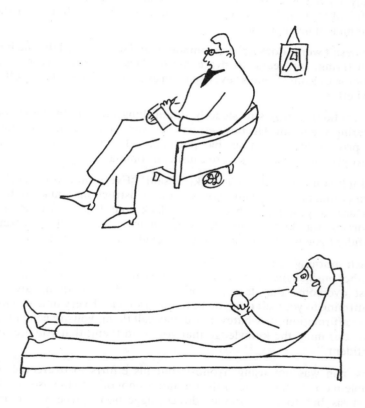

"My problem is that I am a compulsive liar, and that's the truth"

Self-Hypnosis and its Limitations

"Every morning, after I have washed, shaved, dressed myself ready for work and had my breakfast, I stand in front of the mirror before leaving home and look myself straight in the eye. I tell myself that 'today I am going to achieve, today I am going to be completely confident in what I am doing'," the tall Australian told me near the beginning of his first visit.

"It doesn't work, does it?" I commented, and he admitted that he had been trying, for years, to overcome his lack of confidence by this variation of Emile Coue's "every day, in every way, I am getting better and better."

His confidence was still steadily diminishing and his business was suffering as a result. His business worries were being carried over into his private life and thus his personal relationships were being destroyed and his worries were causing insomnia.

"I'll tell you why it doesn't work," I said. "Every time you stand in front of that mirror and give yourself those instructions you know that you are only doing so because you lack confidence. You are re-enforcing the knowledge that you cannot achieve. If you were confident you would not need to go through that ritual every day.

"Each morning, before you face the world, you are giving yourself another push on that downward spiral, you are telling yourself that you must overcome that lack of confidence and in so doing are re-confirming to yourself that you have this problem. Every time you use these affirmations or whatever you may call them, you are cementing into your mind the knowledge that you need them, that you are un-confident."

This man was not using hypnosis but his efforts to overcome his problem do illustrate one of the limitations not only to the use of self-hypnosis but to any form of direct suggestion – whether to the conscious mind or the sub-conscious; whether in hypnosis or not; whether the suggestions are given by the individual with the problem or by another person be they a counsellor, hypnotherapist, psychiatrist, minister of religion, or any other person who tries to use words in this way.

Frequently we are asked whether we can teach someone self-hypnosis. Usually the enquirer admits that they wish to use it to overcome tension, examination nerves, overeating or some other specific problem and, in these cases, we refuse to teach them.

We are Curative Hypnotherapists. Our job is to use our best endeavours to enable a person to cure themselves and, while a person who suffers from abnormal tension will naturally experience benefit from relaxation, this can only be temporary. The sub-conscious has information which dictates a 'need' for this symptom and this must re-assert itself. The tension sufferer will gradually find that the beneficial effect of self-hypnosis will wear off quicker and quicker until they find that the moment they come out of hypnosis they are once again as tense as before they relaxed.

Their resistance may grow until they find it impossible to induce relaxation in themselves at all. They may settle down with the intention of relaxing but with a feeling of impatience, a feeling of guilt about the work they should be doing or simply a feeling that they are so tense that they cannot relax. They may very easily find that their tension makes it 'impossible' to find the time to relax.

This is the reason for the great piles of 'hypnotic' audio-tapes that litter my office, having been brought in by new patients. "I bought this tape but can't relax with it" say a good number of them. Others have actually been to a Hypnotherapist: "I was really relaxed each time I went and the therapist recorded each session for me. I lost weight in the beginning but, although I've been using this tape every day since treatment finished, I'm now 12lbs heavier than when I first went for treatment." – How's that for resistance?!

Self-hypnosis does, however, have beneficial and useful effects for those who do not use it to try to overcome a problem. Perhaps a few brief cases will demonstrate:

A State Registered Nurse came to me for treatment for her weight. Her husband, a medically qualified doctor who had studied homeopathy and was using it to a great extent in his practice, later attended for treatment for his lack of confidence. We solved his problem for him and then taught him self-hypnosis.

When I saw him a couple of months later he told me that this last session with me was the best value for money he had ever experienced. Amongst other things he had taught himself to touch-type in four days.

Being a two-finger man myself, this time-scale has little meaning for me but I understand that it normally takes many times as long as this to achieve accuracy and speed on a typewriter. His method was simply to put himself into hypnosis and then tell himself that he would be able to concentrate; that outside noises would not bother him (except danger which he would be unable to ignore); that his concentration would be total and that he would not break off for the occasional cup of coffee that we all use as an excuse from time to time.

For somebody without a studying problem, self-hypnosis can enhance their abilities to a considerable extent. I would estimate that around 60% of our studying time is wasted by occasional noises that distract us, by stray thoughts that come into our heads, by physical sensations such as an itch that bother us. The average person without a problem in studying could more than double their speed of learning and have the added advantage that they would be able to recall information they have absorbed more easily and more accurately.

A girl who worked with me had toothache, so I sent her to a dentist and, having been assured that nothing was wrong and the pain was simply caused by her wisdom tooth emerging, I taught her to take herself into hypnosis within a few seconds, alleviate her discomfort, and then be back at work in less than two minutes.

One must have caution about taking away pain. It would have been just as easy to have enabled her to take away the pain caused by a massive abscess under a tooth. In that case she would probably not have bothered to have dental treatment and thus have suffered greater damage. Great care, indeed, must be used when dealing with physical discomfort of any sort.

People find the most astonishing uses for self-hypnosis — from touch-typing to learning languages; from (carefully) alleviating aches to taking themselves into sleep in noisy surroundings and another lady found a way of utilising it to fill what would have been many hours of wasted time.

She had come from the north of Scotland to one of the introductory days that I hold 3 or 4 times a year for those interested in training as Curative Hypnotherapists. For her this involved a 10-hour coach trip in each direction.

In the mornings of those days I explain how hypnosis can be used to cure, then over lunch, those who attend can discuss amongst themselves how our methods compare with those taught by other courses about which they may have enquired or in which they have participated. In the afternoon we teach them self-hypnosis and, although we finish about 5pm, this lady's coach did not leave until 11 o'clock in the evening so we chatted a lot more about hypnotherapy for a number of hours then I took her to the coach station.

She later 'phoned to say that she had taken herself into hypnosis as the coach left Birmingham and it appeared to be only a few minutes before she arrived in Glasgow – 5 hours later. She took herself back into relaxation for the second leg of the journey and arrived at her destination after a further 5 hours where her family was waiting to collect her from the coach station.

This was at 9 o'clock in the morning and, as she had been travelling all night, they expected her to be fit for nothing except collapsing into her bed. However she apparently felt like "hitting the town". Yet during the journey she had been absorbing the hours of hypnotherapy talk and sorting out where it fitted in with her previous ideas on the subject.

The final example on self hypnosis that I would like to mention here is a case of non-deliberate use of this state of relaxation to achieve an unexpected result.

A man who attended one of these introductory days took off his glasses before we started teaching self-hypnosis and when he came out of relaxation he said that he could read a notice on the wall which had previously been nothing but a blur with his unaided sight. Five minutes later he was once again unable to read it without his glasses.

I leave you to judge whether his eyesight could be permanently improved.

From time to time one gets a 'clever' patient who, having experienced the techniques we employ to obtain information from the subconscious and having learnt self-hypnosis, will attempt to give themselves treatment. I have never heard of anyone who succeeded and the reasons are obvious.

First of all, one may have difficulty in achieving a deep enough state of relaxation. You reach a certain depth when you are too relaxed to bother to take yourself deeper. It is too much of an effort because you are doing the work instead of leaving it to your therapist.

In the second place, having achieved a sufficiently relaxed state one is certainly too relaxed to use the conscious mind to analyse the answers and formulate questions which are directly to the point.

The third and major obstacle to self-therapy is that the person with the problem has some wrong information in their sub-conscious and they are influenced by this. It is there, they believe it, it is the truth to them and they will look at everything in the light of that 'truth'. They cannot disassociate themselves from it.

One may also get a patient who is 'used to relaxation' and wants to follow their previously learnt path. I am not qualified to compare the relaxation achieved by yoga or meditation with that of hypnosis, particularly as relaxation is experienced slightly differently by everyone. However, those who have previously used these other methods of relaxation tell me that hypnosis is a much deeper state and with those who insist on relaxing themselves, we either fail in the therapy or revert to my normal methods to achieve results.

Self-hypnosis cannot cure, but is certainly useful for those who have no problem, as relaxation is beneficial for everyone and it can be used to enable a person to achieve their full potential in any chosen aspect of their life – so long as there is no information in their sub-conscious to prevent this taking place. The same remarks obviously apply to commercial 'hypnotic' or 'self-help' audio-tapes and to the commercially produced videos which are now being sold and which are usually only purchased by those who have a problem. (One company actually states on their video-cassette covers that their cassettes get to the cause of various problems but, naturally, they do not explain how).

These tapes, like self-hypnosis or the therapist who uses 'direct suggestion', are simply trying to overlay an existing 'truth' with a different one. These methods cannot uncover the misinformation that is causing a problem and we have to ask ourselves whether a computer (our sub-conscious) can have two completely different 'truths' in answer to a single question.

At best the answer to this can only be confusion.

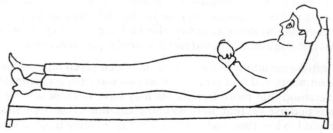

"Just imagine you're floating"

The Magic of Hypnosis

"I am about to terminate my treatment with ————— ————— for a frequent urination problem which I am convinced has been successfully dealt with. The problem is already receding steadily and will go on doing so. For this I am extremely grateful"

Thus started a letter to me in my capacity as president of the Association to which I belong.

This long letter then went on to complain that "poor questioning techniques may be delaying the resolution of problems."

This person had been suffering from the need to continually run to the toilet for **seven years,** yet went on to say "I had five sessions in all, is it not possible that I had superfluous sessions? Perhaps I deserve a refund?"

A problem for 7 years, dealt with in just **two-and-a-half hours** treatment (this Hypnotherapist works, as I do, in half-hour sessions). In that short time the cause of the problem had been recalled from the patients subconscious and corrected – fully corrected, not just suppressed. The therapist had ensured that there was nothing whatsoever that could cause a recurrence. The cure was complete and permanent.

The record card on the patient, (which I needed to answer the letter properly and which the letter gave me permission to borrow), showed that there had been no **symptom treatment** – the whole of the time in each session had been devoted to uncovering and correcting the cause, then in checking to make sure that this had been corrected and that there was nothing else that could create a similar problem in the future.

At the initial consultation the patient had been given an estimate of seven treatments and had accepted that this was only an estimate. It was understood that more treatments may have been necessary and also it was understood that there was no guarantee of success. Success was obtained in less time and at less cost than estimated, yet a refund was requested.

The last paragraph of the letter mentioned how much the patient had enjoyed my book "Hypnotherapy Explained" and how it had brought home "the advantages of this method over direct suggestion." It went on about our work being "very valuable" in relieving "very burdensom symptoms which sometimes cripple the ability to enjoy life almost completely" – yet still a refund was requested.

How would this person have felt if the therapist had finished treatment after three sessions and the problem had returned some time later? What would have been their opinion of Hypnotherapy then?

Think again of the remarks about 'rapport' made previously in this book. The treatment was successful yet this person is almost accusing the therapist of being a confidence trickster and giving them unnecessary treatment. Just how much rapport had been established? And how necessary is this mysterious thing called 'rapport'? As I have already said, it is merely establishing communication.

In spite of reading, in spite of explanations, in spite of actually experiencing, this person still believed that there was some sort of magic in the use of hypnosis. Curative Hypnotherapy is, however, **a logical and methodical treatment.**

People will attend for a consultation at which I normally get them to experience relaxation just to see how they respond and to get rid of any fears they may have about being 'controlled'. That is all I do at their first visit apart from a few very exceptional circumstances, yet occasionally, a person will return to commence the real treatment a few days later and say that their symptoms have not changed at all. All we do is satisfy ourselves that the patient is prepared to follow my words into relaxation yet some expect to be well on the way to recovery! They believe that hypnosis has some sort of magical power to alleviate.

A very small number of people, of course, do not return after this first visit and when I first started in practice I tried to find out why. The usual reason was "I felt beautifully relaxed when I left you and my problem did not worry me so much, but it came back again". Again the belief that this relaxation that we call hypnosis held some sort of magic or that the therapist was in possession of special powers.

Way back in 1891, Ringier (Erfolge des Therapeutischen Hypnotismus in der Landpraxis, Lehmann, Munich) pointed out that there is a greater tendency to break off treatment if it is hypnosis that is being utilised rather than orthodox medical therapy. He commented that the patient expects wonders and is normally disappointed. The simplicity of the treatment does not come up to their expectations and the first signs of symptom improvement often come unnoticed in contrast to the more immediate effect of physical treatment.

Admittedly, Ringier was not a Curative Hypnotherapist and we have come a very long way in understanding the logic of the sub-conscious in the last hundred years, but many people still expect a dramatic change in their problems. In spite of explanations at the consultation a number of people will still measure what happens and how they feel against their pre-conceived ideas no matter how far from the truth these may be.

Everyone who has not experienced hypnosis has a fantasy about what it is like, of how they will feel, of how conscious they will be, of how much they will be in control, of how much power the therapist possesses. Yet a Hypnotherapist is simply a person who has learned a technique to enable a person to relax themselves and a Curative Hypnotherapist has only added to that the understanding to enable him to find the logical progression between cause and effect. We have no special powers – otherwise would we allow our patients to cease treatment before success has been achieved?

As Ringier said, the change in a person may be almost imperceptible while treatment is in progress as in the case of the man who was unemployed due to his fear of examinations and interviews. He was well qualified and had had numerous interviews for jobs arranged for him but was unable to attend any of them because of his phobia.

We were near the end of his treatment. We had isolated the cause but I needed to check that we had corrected it fully and that there was nothing else that could create a similar problem later on.

He failed to keep his appointment and a few days later I received a letter apologising for the fact that he was "such a difficult and slow case to deal with" and also for the fact that he had not had the chance to give me warning that he would be unable to come as arranged, due to the fact that he had been busy finding himself somewhere to live as he had now got a job in a city 100 miles away.

Unemployed for several years because of his fear of interviews. Then successfully passing an interview and working again after only five treatments of half an hour each. Yet he couldn't see any change in himself!

The change in a persons' reaction can often be speeded up by the use of direct suggestion under hypnosis but a therapist has to weigh carefully just when this should be done.

Sometimes it may appear advantageous to suppress symptoms to a limited extent at the beginning of treatment to give the patient the feeling that something CAN be done about their problem. But as the therapist cannot know exactly how the patient will react to his words, the dangers in this are threefold:

It is possible that the patient may leave feeling better and thus not return for proper treatment. When the symptoms return then the word will be spread that "Hypnotherapy is a waste of time".

The patient may react so fully to the suggestions given that they suppress the symptoms completely and create another problem to replace them.

The therapists' words may conflict with the information in the patient's subconscious which will then be unable to accept them. The patient will, therefore feel no beneficial effect with the resultant reaction, once again, that "Hypnotherapy is a waste of time".

So, I NEVER use symptom suppression at the beginning of treatment. I just hope that my explanations of the method of treatment have been understood and accepted. If not, I may lose a patient but at least their problems have not been aggravated.

To use direct suggestion in this way during the investigative process but before the cause of the problem has been uncovered, carries similar disadvantages, although once the stage in treatment is reached where the patient fully understands that there is a reason, a logical reason, for their problem and that this can be corrected then the likelihood of ceasing treatment is vastly diminished.

The only time that I would use symptom suppression in the middle of treatment is when this stage has been reached and the person has a special occasion with which to immediately contend such as an examination. But I would think long and hard before doing so.

In other words it is a very rare that I use direct suggestion to suppress symptoms before the end of treatment and, in most cases, it is then no longer necessary.

A good example of the redundancy of symptom suppression occurred on a 1988 training course when a psychology graduate came, very nervously, as one of the volunteer patients to be treated in front of those on the course.

She told us she had an 'eating problem'. She said that she binged then 'got rid of' the food she had eaten. She would not use the expression that she 'made herself sick' or that she 'vomited'. Neither would she use the name for her problem – 'Bulimia' – although she knew that was the correct description. She did, however, admit that she had developed Anorexia Nervosa at the age of 14.

She was now in her mid-twenties and really miserable. She lacked confidence and felt permanently depressed with these feeling becoming steadily worse.

After the consultation and initial relaxation, she had just 6 treatments before the course finished and I then asked her to come back in two or three weeks for a check-up without charge (volunteer patients are not charged for their treatment). I requested her to come back for two reasons the first being that, although I felt confident that her problem was permanently behind her, I also felt that we needed to check and re-check. I wanted to be absolutely certain.

My second reason was that, while the written examination takes place on the last day of the course, oral examinations are a month later and when course members return on that day they always ask if I have heard from those they have seen having treatment. This girl had come in such a distressed state on the first day that I knew everyone would be checking up to see whether her improvement had been maintained.

Apparently, while I was busy with a patient during the week in which her check-up had been arranged, she telephoned and left a message to say that she did not feel a further treatment was necessary, that she was improving daily.

Then, unexpectedly, the postman delivered an audio tape from her. This girl just bubbled out of the tape – confident and self-assured. There was no mistaking the tone of her voice, it was the same voice but with a completely different and happy personality. She said that she was still improving but admitted that she was not yet fully cured. She KNEW she would never make herself sick again but still had minor problems when eating in the home of someone else. I knew then that she was cured – all she had to do was lose the last remaining bits of her habit which she will have done long before these words were put on paper.

That, of course, was the right time to use direct suggestion but she felt that these last remaining problems would steadily disappear without more treatment and that she needed no further help.

With her background of psychology it is doubtful if she really believed, when she first came for treatment, that we would be able to sort out her problem. But in spite of this background she was prepared to accept and she now understands how she created her problem and why her sub-conscious thought it was necessary.

She understands the logical path that her computer followed and she certainly knows that there is no magic involved in Hypnotherapy.

But others are not so sure. One still gets occasional patients like the nurse who was told by a surgeon, at the hospital at which she works, that if she came for Hypnotherapy she would be 'dabbling in Satanic practices'. She had full access to all possible medical treatment which had been unable to clear up her stomach ulcer. Surely a man of science, such as he, should be ashamed to try to condemn a person to constant discomfort by damning something about which he obviously had no knowledge.

Presumably the person who telephoned the Association to ask if we could recommend a Christian minister of religion to whom he could go for Hypnotherapy, also had thoughts of the occult, magic, spells or the Devil. As a matter of interest we do have an ordained minister amongst our members but we do not differentiate on the grounds of creed, or colour or in any other way. If a person can satisfy the examiners that they fully understand Curative Hypnotherapy and undertake to use CURATIVE methods then they can become a member.

I have to admit to a feeling of amusement about this caller who insisted that he needed a therapist who was not only a Christian but a practicing minister as well. He said that this was because he was worried that there was no mention of hypnosis in the Bible. Yet he had been through psychiatric treatment, drug therapy and even electric shock treatment. I did not like to ask him the chapter and verse which gave the voltage used in Biblical times.

Obviously, ECT and drugs were 'of the establishment' and he therefore accepted them without question. Just as he had accepted that there was something un-Christian about hypnosis when it is only using a persons own God-given logic to correct an error.

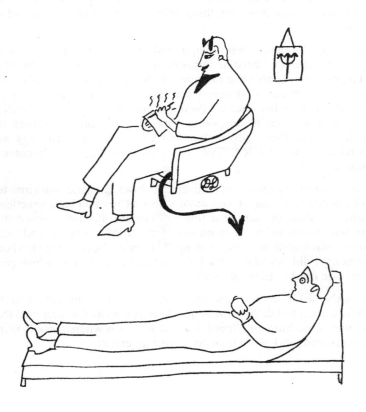

"Are there any side-effects?"

Forensic Hypnosis

"I want you to convince my wife that I'm not having an affair" These were the opening words from the man as I turned to greet the couple in my reception area, after saying goodbye to my previous patient.

From somewhere they had both picked up the idea that a person can be made to tell the truth under hypnosis. That it was impossible to lie when hypnotised.

The husband had, therefore, volunteered to be questioned under hypnosis in front of his wife and also wanted the whole session recorded so that his ammunition was ready the next time he was accused.

Apparently, he had been suffering from his wife's jealousy for 16 years and could not take it any longer. It had to be finally settled or he would get a divorce.

That was his story, BUT:

His wife 'knew' that he was having affairs and believed that if I got him to admit to his infidelity he would be forced to give up his extra-marital activities and the only alternative in her opinion was a divorce.

Of course, I was being asked to do the impossible.

Under Hypnosis a person is still conscious and, while they may remember the truth of a certain situation, nothing can make them divulge it unless they wish to do so and no-one can prevent them using their conscious thoughts to alter whatever facts may not suit their purpose.

In other words a person may keep silent or may tell lies no matter how deep their state of relaxation. In hypnosis, this control always rests with the person who has the information.

I have been approached in the past by two or three people who wished to come on a training course with the object of using hypnosis to uncover evidence for use in Court cases. There is a use in this field but a great deal of caution has to be taken not to lead someone into giving false evidence.

A witness may be hypnotised and asked to recall the numbers on the licence plate of a car seen driving away from the scene of a crime, but this person has volunteered to be hypnotised and to give evidence and will wish to produce something worth-while. If they had not actually seen the licence number they may substitute the number of a car that was passing the scene at the time.

The witness will want to be helpful and, in all good faith, produces false evidence.

Obviously, careful sifting of other evidence should eliminate the driver of the passing car but one can visualise a situation where there may have been a previous connection between this person and the victim of the crime, which could create great suspicion.

M.T.Orne, in "The Potential uses of Hypnosis in Interrogation" (John Wiley & Sons), states: "Hypnosis has **not** been found reliable in obtaining truth from a reluctant witness. Even if it **were** possible to induce hypnosis against one's will, it is well documented that the hypnotised individual still can willfully lie. It is of even greater concern that co-operative hypnotised subjects remember distorted versions of actual events and are themselves deceived. When recalled in hypnosis, such false memories are accompanied by strong subjective conviction and outward signs of conviction that are most compelling to almost any observer. Caution and independent verification are essential in such circumstances."

In Maryland, U.S.A. in 1968 in the case of the State v Harding, the court ruled "Modern medical science recognises that hypnosis can aid in recall, though fancy may be mingled with fact".

Herein lies a further pitfall. A co-operative witness **wants** to help and may easily bring up untruths in furtherance of this desire. The same problem occurs in most uses of hypnosis in therapy because most therapists do not have the ability to see the lack of logic in the creation of symptoms, which only Curative Hypnotherapy methods can sort out.

Remember how, in the case of the 'Boob Grabbers' I suggested a scenario showing how easy it is to lead someone into a completely false confession. In the final chapter of this book, I quote from an article in the Police Gazette how, in interrogation the examiner looks for a little clue, and how Dr. Sargant comments that, if a weak spot is not present the police examiner "can create it by suggestion". Truth and falsehood, as he says, become "hopelessly confused in the mind of both the suspect and the examiner". – And this is without the relaxation of hypnosis when one is less critical.

When you think of the number of innocent people who voluntarily confess to crimes that are later proved to committed by someone else, I shudder to think how a really clever but unscrupulous police examiner could use hypnosis to 'solve' almost all the cases still open in the police files.

Even the so-called 'truth-drug' is often counter-productive in the examination of suspects. As Dr.J.F.Kubis points out: "Those who confess in the drug interview would most likely confess under normal circumstances to a skilled interpreter. It is the criminal who stands to benefit from the technique: he may so contaminate the interview with conflicting information that the physician may become genuinely puzzled as to the validity of his story. And the creation of a doubt as to his guilt is all in favour of the guilty."

Yet the 'truth-drug' is more likely to break down resistance than hypnosis which can only work with a willing subject.

Talking about the lie-detector machine when writing "Instrumental Detection of Deception", C.D.Lee proves this equipment to be most unreliable and points out that the biggest advantage of its use is the impressiveness of the way the machine reacts to every breath and heart-beat which will intimidate most suspects.

He points out that the examiner must have "confidence in himself and the method employed, his persuasiveness, perseverance, and sympathetic attitude towards the suspect. By one means or another the examiner should impart to the subject the idea that he is certain of his guilt, as any indication of doubt on the examiner's part may defeat his purpose.

"Suggest that there was a good reason for his having committed the deed, that he has too much intelligence to have done it without rhyme or reason . . . In the case of theft, suggest that the suspect may have been hungry, or deprived of the necessaries of life; or in homicide, that the victim had done him a great wrong and probably had it coming to him. Be friendly and sympathetic and encourage him to write out or relate the whole story – to clean up and start afresh."

He was talking about the lie-detector, but the same comments apply to the use of hypnosis, and on October 4th. 1988 Channel 3 broadcast a video of the terrifying ordeal of a girl accused of murdering two men. This girl was innocent as was demonstrated by police photographs, but we were shown how her will was steadily eroded and how she was made to believe facts in direct conflict to what had actually happened. This was achieved without the use of hypnosis or any other aid apart from the twisted mind of the interrogator.

The video was of a genuine interrogation and this poor girl ended up signing a confession to being a double murderess. The fact that this action took place in the U.S.A. does not mean it could not happen anywhere else and the fact that the interrogator was deliberately lying to force her to believe she was guilty, does not mean that unskilled questioning, without any overwhelming desire to obtain a confession, could not have achieved similar results.

This girl confessed to murder solely because of clever techniques and the use of hypnosis could have had either no effect or made her accept guilt more readily as her guard would be lowered, her critical faculties less sharp. Her analytical ability would slip more into the background. Relaxation means less alertness. There is no way she could have been persuaded to commit a murder, such a suggestion or instruction would only be accepted by a person already willing to kill. Obtaining a confession could be easy – but the confession may not be true.

One has to bear in mind the lady who was playing with her friend, Mary, in the toilet in the yard behind her parent's shop. You will remember how she created a complete fantasy to cover a truth that was unpalatable to her, and how, when she brought back this false memory, both she and I believed it. Fantasising in this way becomes more natural when your critical faculties are relaxed.

Hypnosis has little place in forensics apart from possibly sharpening the memory but even then everything recalled would have to be carefully corroborated by other means before its acceptance as fact.

To pre-empt the questions of those whom I may meet after they have read this book:

The outcome of the 'Case of the Jealous wife' or is it 'the Case of the Erring Husband' with which I started this chapter, was that the wife had a reason, a very logical reason, in her sub-conscious for her unnatural degree of jealousy. At the time of writing I know they are happy and I wish them well.

Post Hypnotic Suggestion and Hypnotically Induced Amnesia

"I did it because I knew you wanted me to" – a typical remark made by a person 'responding' to a post-hypnotic suggestion; a suggestion given to someone who is in hypnosis with the intention of it being carried out after he or she comes out of relaxation.

Such a suggestion could be to experience a specific feeling such as an itch on their left knee ten minutes later. It could be to remember a certain thing at a given time, or to shout "balderdash" every time the hypnotist uses the word "middle".

My interest in the use of hypnosis is for therapy only, but let us explore post-hypnotic suggestion a little further before we deal with any therapeutic value it may have.

While I have no love for those who damage the reputation of hypnosis as a serious and powerful tool for good, by doing stage tricks, I recently went to a theatre to up-date my impressions of these showmen. During the first half of the performance there were about 15 members of the audience who were on the stage co-operating with the hypnotist.

The last thing that he did before the curtain fell at the interval was to instruct them that they would return to the stage when the show re-started and he told them to "come and join the party".

Only 5 or 6 actually returned to the stage but the same number of fresh people went up also.

These latter had not responded to any 'hypnotic influences' previously so their appearance on the stage was not due to any post-hypnotic suggestion. Therefore the question has to be asked – were those who had been on the stage during the first half of the show responding to a post-hypnotic suggestion, or were they returning because they had enjoyed being in the limelight and wanted to continue the fun?

Certainly, it was very obvious that three of those who went along most completely with the first part of the show were missing after the interval. These were amongst the most susceptible to the showmans' suggestions but decided they had helped enough and rejected his post-hypnotic suggestion.

The "I did it because you wanted me to" response was present in those who returned to the stage for the second part of the show, just as it always will be in a percentage of those with whom I have worked to try to find answers to some of the apparently mystifying aspects of hypnosis.

I have suggested to people under hypnosis that a minute after coming out of relaxation they will have the urge to leave the chair on which they have been sitting and move to another one. Some of them will do so because they knew that I wanted them to, and they will probably do so with a sheepish grin. Others will do so as if it was the most natural thing in the world and when asked "why" will say their new chair looked more comfortable or that they could hear or see better from their new seat.

As with all hypnosis, however, there are those who will not accept, – they accepted hypnosis alright and some of them went into a very deep state of relaxation, but they rejected the idea of moving.

I have mentioned previously in this book two cases of post-hypnotic suggestions which were very similar yet only one of them was effective. The person who was told during 'hypnotherapy' that she would not be able to be hypnotised by anyone else and who, the first time with me, accepted relaxation beautifully; and the man in the audience to which I gave a talk on hypnotherapy who had been given a similar suggestion.

When he came up to me after my talk and apologised for not going along with a little demonstration with which all the others present had co-operated, he told me that he 'knew' he could not be hypnotised by me – which simply meant that he would not even try to go along with my suggestions.

Yet I was not doing a demonstration of hypnosis, only of the ease of accepting suggestion!

Dozens of people have told me on their first visit that they have tried hypnotherapy before and have been told that they are one of the ?? % (fill in whatever number comes into your head) that cannot be hypnotised. I am certain that there must be many more who, on being given this news, never visit another hypnotherapist. Yet, these are straightforward suggestions not given with the help of hypnosis – after all, these people could not accept hypnosis from the person who gave them this 'expert' diagnosis. Yet they still made this persons' suggestions – that they could not be hypnotised – into a reality.

Everyone has a different level of suggestibilty when fully alert and wide awake. We all react to suggestions in different ways, which are largely governed by our previous experiences, and the relaxation of hypnosis cannot alter our experiences.

In other words, a person will accept a post-hypnotic suggestion if they wish to do so, otherwise they will not.

When a schoolboy, I tried the suggestion: "When you go to bed tonight, as soon as your head touches the pillow, you'll think of a hippopotamus" on some of my classmates.

Those who accepted the suggestion, which was given without hypnosis, reported it with awe. Others dismissed the suggestion as silly and forgot all about it. They did not report the failure and if asked, they were not sure whether they had reacted or not. In fact, suggestions like these could, apparently have had complete success.

So where is the strength of post-hypnotic suggestion? When relaxed, a person is, by definition, less analytical and acceptable suggestions are therefore more easily carried out. But a person will still accept only what they wish.

If used with caution and commonsense, a post-hypnotic suggestion can be a valid therapeutic tool. I have mentioned making the saliva of a man taste like honey to ease his sore throat, and he kept the flavour for days until the soreness had gone. One can ease pain and carry the relief forward for a period after hypnosis, or one can enable an overeater to make their stomach feel full on small amounts of food. But all these are stop-gaps which may give an impatient patient the will to continue treatment but do nothing to solve the real problem, and I must repeat that **they have to be used with caution.**

Amnesia is in a very similar position to post-hypnotic suggestion but there are two aspects to this ability-to-forget.

Occasionally, when one is working with a patient they may sit up at the end of the session and ask if I have found out anything useful. These people have been too relaxed to bother about what was going on. They were told not to bring their conscious mind into the treatment and decided to have a day-dream and leave the treatment to the expert. Most of us do a similar thing when we become unaware of the voice or music on a radio and I certainly did a lot of day-dreaming when at school, becoming oblivious to my surroundings until the teacher threw a piece of chalk at me.

However, the number of people who will do this during treatment is very few. Most of us are too inquisitive and wish to know exactly what is going on. Those who can achieve this state are normally very easy to treat and I could call this self-induced amnesia or even spontaneous amnesia.

Then, of course there is the amnesia achieved by acceptance of the hypnotherapists' words. I will not labour this point but simply say that a therapist can only suggest – it is up to the patient to accept or reject. Thus, in reality, this is self-induced amnesia just as all hypnosis is self-hypnosis because everything is done by acceptance and is therefore achieved by the patient themselves.

I can think of no case where amnesia has any therapeutic value whatsoever. The woman who came while I was painting my office wanted me to make her forget her husband. Her words were "I killed him" and she genuinely believed that she had been the cause of his death.

I pointed out that her son had driven her nearly two hundred miles for treatment and if she wiped all memory of her husband from her mind, then she would have extreme difficulty in accepting the existence of her son and that of her other children and granddaughter.

What about her husbands' relatives with whom she had constant contact? Imagine her confusion when she came across old photographs. How could she account to herself for the income she was receiving from an insurance policy on her husband's life?

Obviously, the course of action she suggested would cause serious problems for this lady. Hence, I refused to go along with her wish and we simply found out why she believed that she was responsible for her husbands death. We then enabled her to correct her misunderstanding.

This desire to forget a person is not as uncommon as is often believed – a patient may wish to forget a boy/girl friend who rejected them; another may wish to wipe out all memory of a loved one who has died, because of a continual overpowering sadness – all sorts of apparent good reasons for helping someone forget which if followed without thought could cause terrible problems. The way to treat these people is to find out why they are reacting to death or rejection in the way they are. To suppress the memory is to leave it to seethe in the subconscious because this part of your mind retains everything and all information in a person's memory is available for use in future interpretations.

Some therapists who follow the 'traumatic incident' theory will try to suppress the memory of the trauma. I have already pointed out that traumatic events rarely cause problems and it is the reason for the reaction to the trauma that needs to be uncovered and corrected.

Let us assume that one of these therapists digs up an old traumatic event from a person's past then suggests that it be forgotten. If the patient accepts the suggestion then they can wipe it out of their conscious mind completely, but it cannot be erased from the memory banks of the human computer.

Many of the things that we remember under hypnosis have been 'forgotten' but they can be recalled. The symbols on the number-plate of a car that passed you 10 years ago apparently unnoticed, can be brought back to your conscious mind and a person who forgets what has gone on during a therapy session can recall, by further use of hypnosis, a word by word account of what transpired.

A memory can be bottled-up but it cannot be destroyed, and a therapist who enables a patient to forget a traumatic incident is doing nothing about the reason for the bad reaction to that event. Because of his pre-conceived ideas, he has not even ensured that this particular event has anything to do with the creation of the persons trouble. But let us assume that it has a relevance. To forget is only to wipe it out of the conscious mind but it will always remain in the sub-conscious until something comes along to uncork the bottle and create further problems.

Choosing your Hypnotherapist

Look up the classification of 'Hypnotherapists' in your local Yellow Pages and you will probably find that you have a large choice, all of them with differing descriptions and a bewildering jumble of letters after the names of the various practioners.

Even if you knew the meaning of these letters, it is doubtful if they would give you any guidance as to the type of treatment you are likely to receive. Were you a Hypnotherapist and knew the right questions to ask, you would still have great difficulty in deciding whether any one of those listed, had the understanding of hypnosis to obtain the full benefits for you. After all, it takes a three hour written examination followed by an oral exam for the skilled examination committee referred to in the appendix to satisfy themselves on this point.

You will find people listed with qualifications in nursing, or degrees in science. Do these have any bearing on their ability to use hypnosis to maximum advantage? If they really had this ability would they need to try to give themselves extra credibility by announcing that they have qualifications which have no bearing on the subject. A qualification in structural engineering is just as much help in Hypnotherapy. Does not the fact that someone gives equal prominence in their advertisement to homeopathy, acupuncture or orthodox medicine mean that they cannot be specialists in Hypnotherapy?

How can a therapist reconcile offering both Hypnotherapy and psychotherapy when the average patient will uncover and correct the cause of their complaint in half-a-dozen treatments if hypnosis is correctly used, when psychotherapy takes many years to achieve, in most cases, not a cure, but acceptance of their problem – a learning to live with it.

How does a potential patient sort out a good therapist? This is a simple question but there is no simple answer. Obviously, the easiest procedure is to get a list of addresses from an organisation which sets and maintains strict standards – not just of training but of treatments as well. Right at the start, therefore, you have a difficulty. There are organisations who give lists of practioners many of whom claim to 'cure' but who, in reality, will try to make you believe their preconceived theories and pronounce you cured once you have accepted them.

If, in your area, there should be no member of an organisation on which you can rely then do not just stick a pin in the directory and make an appointment. First consider whether it is worthwhile travelling for proper treatment or get hold of a copy of the literature of each of your local therapists. By spending time going through their printed matter you may be saving yourself a lot of money as well as shortening the period to your cure.

However, once you have the literature you are still not out of the wood, but by reading them through a couple of times very carefully you will probably get the 'feel' of how much understanding each therapist has of the use of hypnosis. But beware! Some people setting up as Hypnotherapists will copy parts of the literature sent out by well established practitioners.

Don't make your choice on the basis of the fees charged, ignore this part of the literature and concentrate on the rest of the contents.

Now comes the crunch: you make your choice, arrange an appointment and attend for a consultation. You will be asked a small amount of background information and should expect to be asked how long you have had your problem and exactly how it affects you. No therapist should be content with the description of your problem given to it by your doctor, psychiatrist or other therapist. He should want to know, **in your own words,** how it affects you. No therapist should be prepared to accept the diagnosis of someone who has been unable to cure you.

Except in cases like a broken bone or virus infection, **a diagnosis can only be confirmed as accurate when it has formed the basis of a cure.**

Your first visit will probably consist of helping to allay any fears that you may have about hypnosis and to a description of this beautiful state of relaxation, and then enabling you to experience it.

The real treatment should begin at your second visit when the search for the cause for your problem will commence. You should expect to be treated as an individual because your problem and its cause are individual to you. You should have person-to-person treatment not just the use of tapes in attempts to alleviate your symptoms.

You should, most certainly, not allow yourself to be 'treated' as part of a group – you, and your problem, are unique.

It cannot be stressed too strongly that to experience the state of hypnosis and be told to lose your problem, is not sufficient. Your practioner should be one who has the ability to enable you to cure yourself and, no later than your second visit, should start the process of finding out how and why you have created your problem.

One lady who came to me for treatment was a compulsive hair-puller – she was continually pulling her hair out of her head. When she recalled the reason for her problem we found that she had originally been a nail-biter and had gone to a local hypnotist. She had been cured of biting her nails by instructions under hypnosis but, because nothing had been done about the CAUSE of this problem, she had developed the alternative of pulling out her hair.

Her nail-biting was a 'need' and once this symptom was removed she developed a far worse habit – to the extent that she had bald patches all over her head. Had the hypnotist understood what he was doing he would have enabled her to recall the reason for her nail-biting and then enabled her to correct that.

If the cause is corrected the problem cannot recur nor can substitute symptoms develop, but to suppress symptoms will usually mean there will be a return of the problem in the future or another problem will be generated in it's place. We all know of people who have treatment of one kind or another and lose that complaint, only to develop another problem shortly thereafter – which when suppressed leads to another, then another. Whether the practioner giving the treatment considers them a neurotic, a hypochondriac, a nuisance or a good source of regular income, it all boils down to one thing – ineffective therapy.

My advice to patients is to ask questions. Will your therapist find out the real cause of your problem? Will she/he then be able to correct it? Does he/she have that ability? If, on your second visit, there is no sign of the therapist knowing how to tackle the problem correctly, then find yourself a genuine Curative Hypnotherapist. Do not be taken in by theories or jargon – the information that will cure lies within yourself and it is the therapist's job to assist you to uncover it.

Remember that mere symptom removal is never the answer, that a therapist who tries to get you to accept his theory of how you have created your problem, is doing you no service whatsoever. Somewhere in your memory is a very logical reason why you have created your problem and until the fault in this logic is located you cannot be cured.

A good therapist will guide you with pointed questions and not just let you ramble on with what is called 'free association' – just talking about whatever comes into your head. It is a nice effortless way for the 'therapist' to make a living , but you are there to get rid of your problem not to boost his income. You will, in fact, find out that in very many cases practioners who use 'free association' will use it only until you come up with something sexual then they will grasp this and work on it until you agree that sex lies at the root of your trouble.

It is amazingly easy to get a person to accept something that is not true. It is easy when a person is not in hypnosis, and therefore much more simple when a patient is relaxed and less critical. It is even more easy to accept when you are dealing with a process about which the patient knows little and is in the hands of a therapist whom he considers to be an expert.

Once a person believes the cause of their problem has been corrected they will naturally look for, and may experience, a lessening of their problem. If the problem is still as bad, then they cannot believe themselves cured. Conversely, if they believe they have been cured the symptoms may recede to some extent – and for a limited period. If, of course, their belief is strong enough they may suppress the symptoms completely and develop another problem in their place.

A case in point was a lady who attended one of my training courses as a volunteer patient a few years ago. She said that she had had Hypnotherapy from a practioner who had found out the cause of her problem and while this had alleviated her symptom for a week or ten days it was now just as bad as before her treatment.

When asked what form her previous treatment had taken she replied that this therapist had "found hatred while she was in the womb". We completed the consultation, commenced treatment and on the fourth session uncovered the true cause of her problem, which was an incident that happened when she was four years old. She corrected the misinterpretation she had made when a child and we know that she has experienced no recurrence of her problem as, not only did her husband come for treatment 6 months later and dispose of his depression, but I have encountered this lady in the street on a couple of occasions since her treatment with me – the latest occasion being only a couple of months prior to writing this account.

Over the few years since she had her treatment I have had two further patients who have been to this same therapist who have both reported that he found "anger in the womb" but they still had their problems. Obviously this therapist was making his patients fit his theories. Instead of finding out from his patients what is creating their problem he is putting ideas into their heads

The mind is very susceptible even when all the critical faculties are fully alert and I would like to quote from the Police Magazine of September 1925:

> ". . . it's pretty hard to get a confession unless you have some little clue to start with on your line of questioning. But, having found

that weak spot, the discrepancies in the man's story begin to widen
until finally he becomes so confused and befuddled that he sees the
game is up."

William Seargent,in "Battle for the Mind" (Wm. Heinemann Ltd)
commenting on these words added:

". . . it is known that truth and falsehood can get hopelessly
confused in the minds of **both** the suspect and the examiner, and
that if what he calls a 'weak spot' is not present, the police
examiner, determined to get a confession, **can create it by
suggestion.**"

He goes on to say:

". . . the eliciting of what turns out later to be false confessions,
believed genuinely by the examiners and suspects alike, recalls a
similar phenomenon in a psycho-therapist's consulting room,
where he begins by believing and conveying to his patient, that
certain childhood traumata have caused his symptoms. After
hours of thought and anxiety, on and off the couch, due to reliving
early fears and guilty feelings concerned with sex, the patient may
come up with details and complicated accounts of emotional
damage done to him on this or that occasion. If the therapist is one
of those who believe in birth traumata and asks about it, the
patient may even begin to remember and to relive this in detail.
The therapist may now be convinced that his particular theory of
birth trauma is correct; yet, what has probably happened is what
may also happen in police examinations; the patient has merely
given back, in all good faith, what was originally implied or
suggested. Yet both the patient and the doctor can genuinely come
to believe in such happenings by using such methods of
investigation; and we must also remember that all present
Freudian theories about the sexual content of the human
subconscious mind have only been arrived at by the use of similar
methods. Falsehoods can come to be believed equally with new
important truths."

In the last few years there has been some publicity about Freud with
particular emphasis on his own peculiarities and it does appear that a
tremendous number of women who went to him for treatment gave
him a history of (often perverted) sexual incidents. This was almost
certainly due to Freud himself unknowingly implanting his ideas in the
minds of his patients. In the book written by Ernest Jones in 1955, he
quoted:

". . . with a patient he (Freud) was treating before the war, whose life history I knew most intimately, I would come across instance after instance where he was believing statements (during psycho-analysis) which I knew to be certainly untrue and also, incidentally, refusing to believe things that were as certainly true."

It is interesting to note Freud's own comments:

"The result at first was hopeless bewilderment. Analysis had lead by the right paths, back to these sexual traumas, and yet they were not true. Reality was lost from under ones feet. At that time I would gladly have given up the whole thing . . . Perhaps I persevered only because I had no choice and could not then begin again at anything else."

It was not because hypnosis did not work that Freud gave it up, it was because he could not fit it into his pre-conceived theories. But it was his theories that were wrong as modern Curative Hypnotherapists are proving daily.

Yet, in spite of the up-to-date understanding of hypnosis we still come across people who are practicing these out-dated theories and, worse still, teaching them to others. Time after time, in book after book, in lecture after lecture, we come across people with theories which they are forcing onto their students. Time after time, poor suffering patients make the rounds of various therapists of different kinds, when many of them could so easily be cured.

The most important thing for a hypnotherapist to remember is that he does have the ability to guide the patient to cure themselves and that the knowledge to do so lies within the mind of the patient.

For a Hypnotherapist to go into treatment with pre-conceived theories of what has caused any particular problem is not only bad for the patient it can, in certain cases, create problems considerably worse.

The patient knows (in their sub-conscious) what has caused their problem, it is the therapist's job to guide them into seeing it – but **the therapist must only be a guide, really nudging the patient from behind rather than trying to show them the way by going first.**

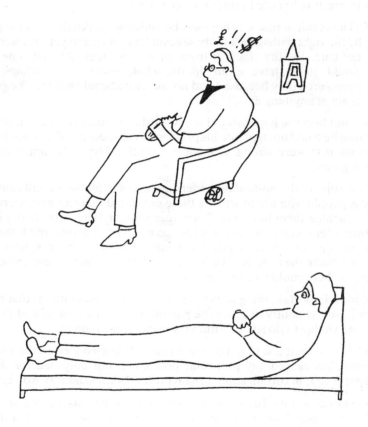

"I have this compulsion to walk out of places without paying"

APPENDIX 1

In 1983, a group of Curative Hypnotherapists who were concerned by the standards of treatment available to the public, set up an **independent examination** body – The CURATIVE HYPNO-THERAPY EXAMINATION COMMITTEE.

These examinations have always been open to anyone, no matter where or how they have obtained their knowledge and understanding of Hypnosis. C.H.E.C. is, therefore, completely independent of any association or training course.

The CERTIFICATE in Hypnotherapy **(C.Hyp)** is only granted after a 3-hour written paper followed by an oral examination.

The DIPLOMA in Hypnotherapy **(D.Hyp)** can only be taken after two years in practice while holding the Certificate. During this period the Diploma applicant must have submitted written work and attended a stated number of hours of recognised further training. The examination itself follows the same format as above (3-hour written then a viva voce).

APPENDIX 2

Curative Hypnotherapists are just people who have learned a job that is more unusual than most. As such they have the beliefs and convictions of any average group of the population. Thus there may be parts of this book which members of the undermentioned organisation feel that I should have left unsaid, It is fair, therefore, to make clear that this book speaks only for myself and from my own experience in practice.

Two years after the setting up of the examination system (see appendix 1) Curative Hypnotherapists founded a **Registered Charity** devoted to improving the understanding and practice of hypnotherapy and enhancing its recognition as a means of curing.

Membership of the ASSOCIATION OF QUALIFIED CURATIVE HYPNOTHERAPISTS (Registered Charity No: 294512) is only available to those who have passed a recognised examination. After which, the Committee of the Association interview applicants before a decision regarding the granting of Membership is made.

The motto of the Association - FIND THE CAUSE TO CURE - incorporates the only really important part of treating any problem. Unless the cause is uncovered a therapist will only be suppressing symptoms and, as such, has no place in the Association.

If symptoms are merely suppressed the problem may re-appear at a later date or a substitute symptom (often worse than the original trouble) may develop.

The Charity will send out, free of charge, a register of qualified Hypnotherapists to any enquirer and will also recommend recognised training courses.

Enquiries should be addressed to the Association at:

A.Q.C.H.
10 Balaclava Road, Kings Heath, Birmingham. B14 75G
phone: (0121) 441 1775

There are
Only two opportunities
each year
to explore the subject of the
Curative use of Hypnosis

Each spring and Autumn the tutors of **Curative Hypnotherapy** hold an introductory Sunday, mainly designed for those who may be interested in training in the most advance techniques of Therapeutic Hypnosis.

The programme includes:-

1. What is hypnosis?

2. The difference between Curative and other uses of hypnosis

3. How Curative Hypnotherapy can cure such a wide variety of problems

4. The opportunity to learn self-hypnosis so that you can take yourself into deep relaxation anytime, anywhere.

5. The chance to talk to others about their experiences/knowledge of hypnosis over a buffet lunch.

6. Questions and answers.

Find out - in a relaxed atmosphere.
An enjoyable and instructive
few hours (10.30am to 5.30pm)
which could change your life.

For details of
Your next opportunity
Contact:-

Therapy Training College
8 & 10 Balaclava Road
Kings Heath, Birmingham. B14 7SG
0121 444 5435

Find The
Cause
To Cure

Members of the Association of Qualified Curative Hypnotherapists
Reg'd Charity No: 294512

The Author

Since 1985 and the publication of David Lesser's first book there has been a steady growth in the acceptance of the use of hypnosis in the treatment of many ailments.

The understanding of hypnosis and its use in therapy has not, unfortunately, improved to the same extent as is shown by correspondence from the public and from practitioners who read "HYPNOTHERAPY EXPLAINED". Hence the need for this second book.

David became a masseur in 1966 and in refining his techniques of relaxation massage and developing methods of teaching them to others, he became interested in the interaction of mind and body – the way such deep mental effects could be achieved by the purely physical treatment of body massage.

He started to investigate the opposite effect – that of mind over body – and this led him into the use of hypnosis, then to hypnotherapy for symptom alleviation and finally into Curative Hypnotherapy.

One of his four daughters is a Beauty Therapist, two are in the world of business and one is a Curative Hypnotherapist. David, himself, devotes about 60 hours a week to hypnotherapy – both treating patients and teaching its curative use to therapists – but still gives a further 12 hours or so each week to relaxing people with massage and teaching this skill for diplomas which are internationally recognised.

In addition to massage qualifications with most leading examination bodies, he is Chairman of the CURATIVE HYPNOTHERAPY EXAMINATION COMMITTEE and also the elected President of the ASSOCIATION OF QUALIFIED CURATIVE HYPNOTHERAPISTS.